GUIDE TO
BAY AREA
RESTAURANTS

by Sue Remick and the Editors of
Bay Area Consumers' CHECKBOOK Magazine

SO-AXA-786

This book is a special publication of the Center for the Study of Services, a nonprofit organization dedicated to helping consumers get the most for their money when they buy services. Founded in 1974 with the help of funding from Consumers Union and the U.S. Office of Consumer Affairs, the Center is now supported primarily by subscribers to the magazines it publishes in the San Francisco Bay Area and the Washington, D.C., area. The magazines, entitled *Bay Area Consumers' CHECKBOOK* and *Washington Consumers' CHECKBOOK*, rate the quality and prices of local service firms of various kinds, ranging from auto repair shops to hospitals to banks.

More copies may be ordered at $7.95 per copy from: *CHECKBOOK's Restaurant Guide*—Subscription Processing, 733 15th Street NW, Suite 820, Washington, D.C. 20005; (510) 763-7979. Make check payable to "Checkbook." Quantity prices available upon request.

Book Design: DR Pollard & Associates Inc.
Cover Design: Creative Partners/The Bluemont Co.

Our sincere thanks to the thousands of *CHECKBOOK* magazine and *Consumer Reports* subscribers whose ratings made this book possible.

CONTENTS

INTRODUCTION

In this guide, we've pulled together in as brief a form as possible a broad range of information to help you find genuine dining pleasure at a fair price.

Many readers will know our nonprofit organization, the Center for the Study of Services, and our magazine, *Bay Area Consumers' CHECKBOOK*, for our in-depth evaluations of hospitals, insurance companies, auto repair services, home maintenance firms, and other types of local services. The basic approach is the same here: our research is careful, thorough, and unbiased; we accept no advertising nor other fees (nor free meals) from the firms we rate; and *we* decide which service firms to rate, whether they want to be included or not.

But restaurants are different in some respects. In most of our other reports, we try to steer you away from trouble; in this guide, we're trying to steer you to a good time. Also, what's good in a restaurant is literally a matter of taste; so there is, and should be, a lot more subjectivity and opinion in this guide than in our other reports.

For each restaurant, you'll find numerical scores showing how the restaurant was evaluated by consumer raters. These raters are *CHECKBOOK* magazine and *Consumer Reports* magazine subscribers who returned our questionnaires with ratings of restaurants they had recently visited. They rated the "food," "service," "ambience," and "value for your money." Possible scores run from 25 ("unacceptable") to 100 ("perfect"), but most restaurants scored between 60 and 90. So that you can understand what's behind the scores, we tell you how many ratings each restaurant received and how consistent the ratings were.

The raters are not master chefs nor professional critics. Rather, they are "real people," from all walks of life. They do, however, have some characteristics in common—an ability to form (and explain) opinions, an enthusiasm for dining out, and a strong interest in getting what they pay for.

As we reviewed the tens of thousands of ratings and comments these raters submitted, we were struck by their keen appreciation for—indeed, excitement about—fine food. But we were equally struck by their ability to look at quality and price separately. As you will see, many restaurants received top marks for food, service, and ambience but weren't, in the opinion of our raters, worth the price. On the other hand, some restaurants that rated lower for the quality of their offerings had such good prices or generous portions that they rated very high for "value."

Beginning on page 8 is our "Quick-Check" Table, which lists 575 restaurants. The table shows how each restaurant was rated by surveyed customers and it tells you whether the ratings were very consistent (VC), consistent (C), mixed (M), or very mixed (VM). The restaurants are separated into sections for Alameda, Contra Costa, Marin/Napa/Solano/Sonoma, San Francisco, San Mateo, and Santa Clara/Santa Cruz/Monterey counties. Within these geographic areas, the restaurants are divided into price categories, based on the range of prices on their menus and a sampling of the prices of the most popular items. Within each location-price category, the restaurants are listed in order of the "food" score they received from our raters. To help you satisfy your taste at the moment, the type of cuisine is given for each restaurant. You can easily go to a location-price category on the Quick-Check Table and run your finger down the list until you find the top-rated, conveniently located restaurant serving a type of cuisine that suits your fancy.

For the 259 restaurants that received the highest ratings from consumers, you will find more extensive information, including brief write-ups, in an alphabetical listing that begins on page 29 and makes up the bulk of the guide. These 259 restaurants are the ones that earned a consumer ratings score of at least 75 for "value for your money" or at least 80 for "food."

While we think the opinions of "real people" are an excellent guide to restaurants you're likely to enjoy, it is interesting to have another perspective for comparison. So we've collected professionals' reviews from the *Contra Costa Times*, the *Oakland Tribune*, the *San Francisco Examiner*, the *San Francisco Chronicle*, the *San Jose Mercury News*, and *Gourmet* magazine. And we've included in our write-ups highlights of those comments, judgments, and recommendations. In addition, the write-ups note any recent honors a restaurant has received—such as awards from *San Francisco Focus* magazine and the *Wine Spectator*.

For the 259 higher rated restaurants included in our alphabetical listing, you'll also find the practical details on location, dress and reservation requirements, credit card acceptance, parking, handicapped access, entertainment, and hours.

We've also included a "Best for Food" list and a "Best for Value" list on the next page. And at the back of the guide, beginning on page 116, there's a list of the highest rated restaurants, grouped by type of cuisine.

Finally, beginning on page 122, you'll find listings of restaurants with such special features as Saturday or Sunday brunch, late hours, entertainment, outdoor dining, scenic view, home delivery, and takeout.

Of the 575 restaurants included on the Quick-Check Table, we included any restaurant (except a number of fast-food/mass-food chains) that received 13 or more ratings from our consumer raters. These are, in other words, the places where our raters eat. Virtually all of our raters live in Alameda, Contra Costa, Marin, San Francisco, San Mateo, or Santa Clara counties, and these places were convenient enough that at least 13 raters had tried them.

Many of the best-known restaurants in the area are included. But so are many little-known places that our "real people" have discovered.

Read, eat, and enjoy.

CHECKBOOK'S BEST

BEST FOOD

Chef Paul's
French Laundry
Le Papillon
The Terrace at The Ritz-Carlton
Domaine Chandon
Emile's
Fleur de Lys
Dal Baffo
Garden City
Iron Gate
Silks—Mandarin Hotel
Barone's
Cha Cha Cha
Helmand
Kirala
La Folie
Masa's
The Plumed Horse
231 Ellsworth
Woodward's Garden
Buon Gusto
Chez TJ
Hunan
Kabul *(Sunnyvale)*
Le Charm
Le Maconnais
Le Mouton Noir
Luzern
Pho 84
Postrio
Rivoli
Rue de Paris
Scala's Bistro
Vivande
Wente Vineyards Restaurant
Zachary's Chicago Pizza *(Oakland)*

BEST VALUE

Pho 84
La Taqueria
Le Maconnais
Eliza's *(San Francisco)*
La Mediterranee
Le Charm
Andale *(Los Gatos)*
Gourmet Carousel
Luzern
Old Spaghetti Factory *(San Jose)*
Phnom Penh House
Banchero's
Cha Cha Cha
Helmand
Country Way
House of Nanking
La Bergerie
Original Joe's *(San Francisco)*
Picante Cocina Mexicana
Spring Garden
Andale (Palo Alto)
Brennan's
Fresh Choice *(Milpitas)*
Lemon Grass
Pasand Madras Cuisine
Spettro
Basque Cultural Center
Bold Knight Cattleman's
Chef Paul's
Italian Colors
Kabul *(Sunnyvale)*
Khan Toke Thai House
La Fiesta
Montecatini
Sam's Bar-B-Que
Sweet Tomatoes *(Sunnyvale)*
The Terrace at the Ritz-Carlton
Three Flames

QUICK-CHECK TABLE

Listed in order of food score within price category and county.
(Number of raters and consistency of ratings shown in parentheses:
VC=very consistent, C=consistent, M=mixed, VM=very mixed.)

ALAMEDA COUNTY

$

			Food	Service	Value
Pho 84–*Oakland* (21-C)	Vietnamese	510-832-1429	86	71	91
Zachary's Chicago Pizza–*Oakland* (27-M)	Pizza	510-655-6385	86	68	81
Lemon Grass–*Livermore* (15-M)	Thai	925-606-6496	83	78	83
Doug's Bar-B-Q–*Emeryville* (16-C)	BBQ	510-655-9048	81	73	81
Zachary's Chicago Pizza–*Berkeley* (15-VM)	Pizza	510-525-5950	81	67	79
Cafe Fanny–*Berkeley* (15-C)	Breakfast/Lunch	510-524-5447	81	71	63
Phnom Penh House–*Oakland* (15-C)	Cambodian	510-893-3825	80	70	86
Picante Cocina Mexicana–*Berkeley* (17-C)	Mexican	510-525-3121	80	65	84
Panini–*Berkeley* (14-C)	Lunch only	510-849-0405	80	70	77
Cha-Am–*Berkeley* (35-C)	Thai	510-848-9664	80	64	75
Boran Thai–*Berkeley* (14-VC)	Thai	510-525-3625	78	71	78
La Mediterranee–*Berkeley* (13-C)	Middle Eastern	510-540-7773	77	74	87
Rasa Sayang–*Albany* (17-VM)	Malaysian	510-525-7000	77	72	76
The Blue Nile–*Berkeley* (17-M)	Ethiopian	510-540-6777	74	68	81
Cactus Taqueria–*Oakland* (27-M)	Mexican	510-547-1305	74	60	75
Siam Cuisine–*Berkeley* (14-VC)	Thai	510-548-3278	74	65	73
Banchero's–*Hayward* (28-C)	Italian	510-276-7355	72	74	85
Fresh Choice–*Pleasanton* (20-C)	American	925-734-8186	72	68	78
Sweet Tomatoes–*Pleasanton* (20-VC)	American	925-463-9285	71	63	81
Rockridge Cafe–*Oakland* (23-C)	American	510-653-1567	71	67	74
Barney's Gourmet Hamburger–*Oakland* (17-M)	American	510-655-7180	71	65	74
Christopher's Nothing Fancy Cafe–*Albany* (19-M)	Mexican	510-526-1185	71	65	72
The Cantina–*Oakland* (28-M)	Mexican	510-482-3663	70	65	72
Long Life Vegi House–*Berkeley* (16-M)	Vegetarian	510-845-6072	69	64	77
Juan's Place–*Berkeley* (14-VC)	Mexican	510-845-6904	69	70	74
Saul's–*Berkeley* (19-VM)	Deli	510-848-3354	69	67	69
Brennan's–*Berkeley* (30-C)	American (Hofbrau)	510-841-0960	68	60	83
Old Spaghetti Factory–*Oakland* (22-M)	Italian	510-893-0222	65	68	75

$$

			Food	Service	Value
Ajanta–*Berkeley* (28-C)	Indian	510-526-4373	84	80	80
Nadine–*Oakland* (16-VC)	Continental	510-482-5303	83	73	76
Nan Yang Rockridge–*Oakland* (21-C)	Burmese	510-655-3298	82	77	81
The Cambodiana's–*Berkeley* (35-C)	Cambodian	510-843-4630	81	75	81
China Chili–*Fremont* (13-M)	Chinese	510-791-1688	81	86	80
Britt-Marie's–*Albany* (32-C)	Continental	510-527-1314	81	75	79
O Chame–*Berkeley* (37-C)	Japanese	510-841-8783	81	77	75
Pizza Rustica Cafe–*Oakland* (30-C)	Pizza	510-654-1601	80	69	78
La Creme de la Creme–*Oakland* (33-M)	French	510-420-8822	80	76	78
Mama Lan's–*Berkeley* (13-C)	Vietnamese	510-528-1790	80	71	74
Zza's Trattoria–*Oakland* (36-C)	Italian	510-839-9124	78	73	76
Venezia–*Berkeley* (48-C)	Italian	510-849-4681	78	70	75
Le Cheval–*Oakland* (26-M)	Vietnamese	510-763-8495	77	70	80
Jade Villa–*Oakland* (17-M)	Chinese	510-839-1688	76	72	76
Bette's Oceanview Diner–*Berkeley* (41-C)	American	510-644-3230	76	66	72
Crogan's Seafood House–*Oakland* (22-M)	American	510-339-2098	76	77	72
Spettro–*Oakland* (13-C)	California	510-465-8320	75	79	83
Walker's Pie Shop–*Albany* (34-C)	American	510-525-4647	75	76	79
Plearn Thai–*Berkeley* (27-M)	Thai	510-841-2148	75	71	78
Fatapple's–*Berkeley* (38-C)	American	510-526-2260	75	72	77
Emil Villa's California BBQ–*Oakland* (26-C)	BBQ	510-654-0915	75	70	76
Rick & Ann's–*Berkeley* (29-M)	American	510-649-8538	75	66	71
Emil Villa's California BBQ–*Hayward* (14-C)	BBQ	510-537-0734	74	70	77
Cafe de la Paz–*Berkeley* (23-C)	Latin American	510-843-0662	74	71	76
King Tsin–*Berkeley* (16-M)	Chinese	510-525-9890	74	67	74
Chevy's–*Alameda* (23-C)	Mexican	510-521-3768	74	67	73
Country Way–*Fremont* (21-C)	American	510-797-3188	73	78	84
Zatis–*Oakland* (13-M)	California/Mediterranean	510-658-8210	72	73	75
Emil Villa's California BBQ–*Fremont* (13-VM)	BBQ	510-790-1992	70	66	69
Caffe Giovanni–*Berkeley* (22-M)	Italian	510-843-6678	69	70	70
Red Lobster–*Fremont* (21-M)	Seafood	510-657-2436	69	65	61
Cafe del Sol–*Berkeley* (17-C)	Continental	510-525-4927	68	69	67
Oakland Grill–*Oakland* (28-M)	American	510-835-1176	66	65	67

$$$

			Food	Service	Value
Chef Paul's–*Oakland* (14-C)	French	510-547-2175	94	86	82
Kirala–*Berkeley* (29-C)	Japanese	510-549-3486	87	74	74
Barone's–*Pleasanton* (19-C)	Continental	925-426-0987	87	83	74
Rivoli–*Berkeley* (61-C)	California	510-526-2542	86	78	81
Lalime's–*Berkeley* (85-C)	Mediterranean	510-527-9838	84	80	79
Solano Grill & Bar–*Albany* (16-C)	East-West	510-525-8686	84	81	77
Citron–*Oakland* (62-C)	Mediterranean	510-653-5484	84	78	75
Chez Panisse Cafe–*Berkeley* (73-M)	California	510-548-5049	84	79	71
Soizic–*Oakland* (19-C)	Bistro	510-251-8100	82	74	79

			Food	Service	Value

$$$ *(continued)*

			Food	Service	Value
Bay Wolf–*Oakland* (76-M)	Mediterranean	510-655-6004	82	80	75
Strizzi's–*San Leandro* (23-VC)	Italian	510-483-4883	82	75	74
Townhouse Bar & Grill–*Emeryville* (28-C)	American	510-652-6151	81	74	75
Oliveto–*Oakland* (41-M)	Italian	510-547-5356	81	76	71
Italian Colors–*Oakland* (16-VC)	Italian	510-482-8094	80	82	82
Pleasanton Hotel–*Pleasanton* (32-C)	California	925-846-8106	79	76	76
Hungry Hunter–*Pleasanton* (13-M)	Steak	925-463-1244	78	79	76
Santa Fe Bar & Grill–*Berkeley* (24-C)	American	510-841-4740	78	78	74
Bucci's–*Emeryville* (49-M)	Italian	510-547-4725	78	73	72
Cafe Enrico–*Alameda* (16-C)	Italian	510-522-0128	77	77	80
Horatio's–*San Leandro* (27-M)	American	510-351-5556	77	75	71
Ginger Island–*Berkeley* (66-M)	Pan Asian	510-644-0444	77	74	70
Hungry Hunter–*Oakland* (22-M)	Steak	510-261-3287	76	73	74
Gertie's Chesapeake Bay–*Berkeley* (57-M)	Seafood	510-841-2722	76	75	71
Hayward Fishery–*Dublin* (20-C)	Seafood	925-828-8882	74	75	74
Yoshi's–*Oakland* (21-M)	Japanese	510-238-9200	74	65	64
New Rochelle–*Pleasanton* (13-M)	Mediterranean	925-846-5740	73	71	79
Maharani–*Berkeley* (16-M)	Indian	510-848-7777	73	66	75
Black Angus–*San Lorenzo* (20-VC)	American	510-276-1400	73	72	73
Jack's–*Oakland* (16-C)	Bistro	510-444-7171	72	73	72
Bateau Ivre–*Berkeley* (19-VC)	French	510-849-1100	72	66	70
Milano–*Emeryville* (35-M)	Italian	510-420-1175	71	69	73
Hayward Fishery–*Hayward* (14-C)	Seafood	510-537-6410	71	70	68
The Cape Cod–*Albany* (13-M)	Continental	510-528-3308	70	75	76
His Lordship's–*Berkeley* (28-M)	Continental	510-843-2733	70	72	67
Cesare's–*Oakland* (14-VM)	Italian	510-531-9400	69	73	70
Spenger's Fish Grotto–*Berkeley* (70-M)	Seafood	510-845-7771	68	65	71
Charley Brown's–*Emeryville* (21-VM)	American	510-658-6580	67	70	70
Overland House–*Oakland* (16-C)	American	510-268-9222	67	64	64
Black Angus–*Fremont* (16-VM)	American	510-794-8222	65	69	63

$$$$

			Food	Service	Value
Le Maconnais–*Hayward* (14-C)	French	510-538-3522	86	85	89
Wente Vineyards Restaurant–*Livermore* (35-C)	American	925-456-2450	86	83	75
Papillon–*Fremont* (19-M)	French	510-793-6331	85	80	76
Massimo's–*Fremont* (15-C)	Italian	510-792-2000	83	79	79
Rue de Main–*Hayward* (15-C)	French	510-537-0812	83	82	73
Kincaid's Bay House–*Oakland* (39-C)	Seafood	510-835-8600	79	77	75
Trader Vic's–*Emeryville* (14-C)	Polynesian	510-653-3400	79	85	73
Scott's Seafood Grill–*Oakland* (42-M)	Seafood	510-444-3456	77	76	68
Il Pescatore–*Oakland* (20-C)	Italian	510-465-2188	77	76	68
Hong Kong East Ocean–*Emeryville* (32-C)	Chinese	510-655-3388	76	61	69
Skates on the Bay–*Berkeley* (69-M)	Seafood	510-549-1900	75	73	71

$$$$$

			Food	Service	Value
Chez Panisse Restaurant–*Berkeley* (29-VM)	California	510-548-5525	84	80	72

CONTRA COSTA COUNTY

		Food	Service	Value

$

Uncle Chung's–*Pinole* (15-C)	Chinese	510-222-8881	83	84	81
Pasta Cuisine–*Orinda* (14-M)	Italian	925-254-5423	74	62	79
Fresh Choice–*Concord* (28-C)	American	925-671-7222	72	67	81

$$

Montecatini–*Walnut Creek* (14-M)	Italian	925-943-6608	85	79	82
Spring Garden–*Concord* (17-C)	Chinese	925-827-1900	84	84	84
Max's Diner–*San Ramon* (16-C)	American	925-277-9300	83	80	81
Pasta Primavera Cafe–*Walnut Creek* (16-VC)	Italian	925-930-7775	80	73	70
Magic Garlic–*Walnut Creek* (40-M)	Mediterranean	925-938-6868	77	68	73
Uncle Yu's–*Lafayette* (19-C)	Chinese	925-283-1688	76	77	76
Chevy's–*Pleasant Hill* (33-C)	Mexican	925-685-6651	76	75	75
Crogan's Bar & Grill–*Walnut Creek* (25-M)	American	925-933-7800	76	73	74
Fatapple's–*El Cerrito* (64-C)	American	510-528-3433	75	71	75
Emil Villa's California BBQ–*Concord* (26-M)	BBQ	925-827-9902	75	76	72
Back Forty Texas BBQ–*Pleasant Hill* (44-C)	BBQ	925-935-1440	73	73	75
Olive Garden–*Pittsburg* (19-C)	Italian	925-778-6208	73	74	74
Cafe Select–*Kensington* (24-C)	American	510-525-1350	73	72	70
Abernathy's–*Walnut Creek* (23-C)	American	925-934-9490	72	73	77
El Torito–*Concord* (27-M)	Mexican	925-798-7660	72	73	75
Inn Kensington–*Kensington* (20-M)	California	510-527-5919	72	71	73
Marie Callender's–*Concord* (24-C)	American	925-827-4930	72	72	71
Lyon's–*Walnut Creek* (20-C)	American	925-935-4666	71	67	77
Chili's–*Walnut Creek* (23-M)	Tex-Mex	925-933-1251	71	72	73
Strings–*Walnut Creek* (14-VM)	Italian	925-938-1492	71	70	73
Alexander Ristorante–*Orinda* (19-M)	Italian	925-253-1322	71	70	62
CC Ole's–*Concord* (25-C)	Mexican	925-798-1800	69	70	78
Chevy's–*El Cerrito* (30-C)	Mexican	510-526-2551	68	67	70
Marie Callender's–*Walnut Creek* (21-M)	American	925-943-7100	68	69	70
Black Diamond Brewing–*Walnut Creek* (17-M)	American	925-943-2330	68	74	70
El Charro–*Lafayette* (26-VM)	Tex-Mex	925-283-2345	66	70	71
T R's Bar & Grill–*Concord* (19-VM)	California	925-827-4660	64	69	59

$$$

Miraku–*Lafayette* (14-C)	Japanese	925-284-5700	85	84	78
Le Marquis–*Lafayette* (14-M)	French	925-284-4422	85	86	77
Salute at Marina Bay–*Richmond* (14-VC)	Italian/Seafood	510-215-0803	84	77	77
La Cocotte–*Clayton* (13-C)	French	925-672-1333	84	78	76
Spiedini–*Walnut Creek* (41-C)	Italian	925-939-2100	81	73	73
Max's Opera Cafe–*Walnut Creek* (60-C)	American	925-932-3434	80	78	80
Hungry Hunter–*Concord* (17-M)	Steak	925-676-1677	79	78	76
Humphrey's–*Antioch* (23-C)	American	925-778-5800	79	82	73
Tao's Grill–*Walnut Creek* (14-C)	Italian	925-934-3850	79	76	72
Lark Creek Cafe–*Walnut Creek* (31-C)	American	925-256-1234	79	77	67

$$$ *(continued)*

			Food	Service	Value
Spruzzo!–*Lafayette* (34-C)	Italian	925-284-9709	78	75	79
Casa Orinda–*Orinda* (32-C)	American/Italian	925-254-2981	78	74	75
Miraku–*Walnut Creek* (16-C)	Japanese	925-932-1112	77	77	71
Faz–*Danville* (56-M)	Mediterranean	925-838-1320	77	73	69
Yokohama–*El Cerrito* (13-C)	Japanese	510-234-0821	76	72	79
Grissini–*Concord* (29-M)	Italian	925-680-1700	76	75	72
Hotel Mac–*Pt Richmond* (26-M)	American	510-233-0576	76	76	69
Hungry Hunter–*Lafayette* (36-C)	Steak	925-938-3938	75	76	74
Cape Cod House–*Lafayette* (25-C)	Seafood	925-283-8288	74	74	74
Front Room–*Concord* (19-M)	American	925-688-1600	74	74	68
Petar's–*Lafayette* (25-VM)	Continental	925-284-7117	73	72	73
Black Angus–*Pleasant Hill* (38-C)	American	925-938-9900	71	68	72
Pacific Fresh–*Pleasant Hill* (39-M)	Seafood	925-827-3474	71	70	66
Johnny Angels–*Walnut Creek* (22-M)	California	925-939-6949	71	71	64
Nantucket Fish Company–*Crockett* (21-M)	Seafood	510-787-2233	69	68	68
Peppermill–*Concord* (18-C)	American	925-671-2233	67	65	65

$$$$

			Food	Service	Value
Prima–*Walnut Creek* (33-M)	Italian	925-935-7780	82	76	76
Mudd's–*San Ramon* (41-M)	California	925-837-9387	79	76	72
Bridges–*Danville* (48-M)	East-West	925-820-7200	79	76	70
Scott's Seafood Grill–*Walnut Creek* (43-M)	Seafood	925-934-1300	78	77	71
Duck Club–*Lafayette* (34-M)	American	925-283-7108	76	75	69
Blackhawk Grille–*Danville* (37-M)	California	925-736-4295	75	75	69
California Cafe–*Walnut Creek* (55-M)	California	925-938-9977	74	77	68

MARIN/NAPA/SOLANO/SONOMA COUNTIES

$

			Food	Service	Value
Royal Thai–*San Rafael* (21-C)	Thai	415-485-1074	80	73	77
Jennie Low's–*Mill Valley* (30-VM)	Chinese	415-388-8868	72	66	73

$$

			Food	Service	Value
The Diner–*Yountville* (14-M)	California/Mexican	707-944-2626	84	79	78
D'Angelo–*Mill Valley* (23-C)	Italian	415-388-2000	78	74	73
Le Chalet Basque–*San Rafael* (14-C)	Basque	415-479-1070	77	78	79
Fabrizio's–*Larkspur* (21-C)	Italian	415-924-3332	77	77	78
Good Earth–*Larkspur* (28-C)	California	415-461-7322	77	71	76
Piatti–*Sonoma* (14-C)	Italian	707-996-2351	77	70	71
Bubba's Diner–*San Anselmo* (14-C)	American	415-459-6862	72	62	64
Gira Polli–*Mill Valley* (18-M)	Italian	415-383-6040	69	67	67
Panama Hotel–*San Rafael* (15-M)	American	415-457-3993	68	68	70
Chevy's–*Greenbrae* (29-M)	Mexican	415-461-3203	67	68	71
Cantina–*Mill Valley* (14-M)	Mexican	415-381-1070	67	66	70
Emil Villa's California BBQ–*Corte Madera* (19-C)	BBQ	415-927-7427	58	63	63

MARIN/NAPA/SOLANO/SONOMA *(continued)*

$$$

			Food	Service	Value
Guernica–*Sausalito* (13-VC)	Basque	415-332-1512	84	72	80
Mustards Grill–*Napa* (58-M)	American	707-944-2424	83	77	76
Tra Vigne–*St Helena* (67-M)	Italian	707-963-4444	83	79	76
Christophe–*Sausalito* (21-C)	French	415-332-9244	82	79	79
Catahoula–*Calistoga* (14-M)	American	707-942-2275	79	74	70
Brava Terrace–*St Helena* (13-M)	California	707-963-9300	78	77	76
De Schmire–*Petaluma* (14-C)	Continental	707-762-1901	78	72	73
Salute–*San Rafael* (26-C)	Italian	415-453-7596	78	73	73
Guaymas–*Tiburon* (59-C)	Mexican	415-435-6300	78	71	72
Joe Lo Coco's–*Greenbrae* (25-M)	Italian	415-925-0808	78	77	70
Left Bank–*Larkspur* (27-C)	French	415-927-3331	77	70	74
Buckeye Road House–*Mill Valley* (77-C)	California	415-331-2600	77	72	72
Il Fornaio—St Claire Hotel–*Corte Madera* (41-C)	Italian	415-927-4400	77	71	70
Spinnaker–*Sausalito* (15-C)	California	415-332-1500	75	74	73
Bistro Don Giovanni–*Napa* (14-C)	Italian	707-224-3300	74	74	70
Bistro Alsacienne–*Mill Valley* (14-C)	French/German	415-389-0921	74	74	69
Adriana's–*San Rafael* (27-M)	Italian	415-454-8000	73	74	71
Tutto Mare–*Tiburon* (14-VM)	Italian	415-435-4747	73	72	69
Cacti–*Novato* (24-VC)	Tex-Mex	415-898-2234	72	70	69
Sam's Anchor Cafe–*Tiburon* (27-M)	American	415-435-4527	67	68	68
Hilltop Cafe–*Novato* (20-M)	California	415-892-2222	64	63	63

$$$$

			Food	Service	Value
Manka's Inverness Lodge–*Inverness* (18-C)	California	415-669-1034	84	69	64
John Ash & Co–*Santa Rosa* (18-VM)	California	707-527-7687	83	87	76
Lark Creek Inn–*Larkspur* (79-C)	California	415-924-7766	83	80	73
Bay View Restaurant–*Bodega Bay* (16-VC)	Continental	707-875-2751	82	74	77
El Paseo–*Mill Valley* (21-C)	French	415-388-0741	82	83	74
The Caprice–*Tiburon* (15-C)	California	415-435-3400	81	77	76
Mikayla–*Sausalito* (27-M)	California	415-331-5888	77	79	69
California Cafe–*Corte Madera* (37-C)	California	415-924-2233	74	72	70
Marin Joe's–*Corte Madera* (24-VM)	Italian	415-924-2081	72	67	74

$$$$$

			Food	Service	Value
French Laundry–*Yountville* (16-C)	French	707-944-2380	93	88	77
Domaine Chandon–*Yountville* (45-C)	French	707-944-2892	91	88	75
Auberge du Soleil–*Rutherford* (28-M)	California	707-967-3111	85	85	73

SAN FRANCISCO

$

			Food	Service	Value
Cha Cha Cha–*Upper Haight* (14-C)	Caribbean	415-386-5758	87	74	85
La Taqueria–*Mission* (14-C)	Mexican	415-285-7117	85	76	89
House of Nanking–*Chinatown* (16-M)	Chinese	415-421-1429	85	59	84
Pauline's Pizza Pie–*Mission* (13-C)	Pizza	415-552-2050	85	71	68

		Food	Service	Value

$ *(continued)*

			Food	Service	Value
Eliza's–*Civic Center* (19-VC)	Chinese	415-621-4819	84	79	88
Khan Toke Thai House–*Richmond* (13-M)	Thai	415-668-6654	83	78	82
Ti-Couz–*Mission* (35-VC)	French (Crepes)	415-252-7373	80	66	77
Vicolo–*Civic Center* (37-M)	Pizza	415-863-2382	80	68	76
Mandalay–*Richmond* (18-M)	Burmese	415-386-3895	76	71	78
Esperpento–*Valencia* (15-M)	Spanish	415-282-8867	76	68	77
Gourmet Carousel–*Pacific Heights* (13-C)	Chinese	415-771-2044	75	68	86
Sears Fine Foods–*Union Square* (16-M)	American	415-986-1160	75	75	75
Mom Is Cooking–*Excelsior* (17-VM)	Mexican	415-586-7000	74	57	77

$$

			Food	Service	Value
Le Charm–*South of Market* (21-C)	Bistro	415-546-6128	86	81	87
Hunan–*North Beach* (19-C)	Chinese	415-956-7727	86	72	78
Fringale–*South of Market* (78-C)	Bistro	415-543-0573	85	78	78
Yank Sing–*Financial District* (55-C)	Chinese	415-362-1640	84	73	71
Angkor Wat–*Richmond* (27-C)	Cambodian	415-221-7887	82	81	81
Eliza's–*Potrero Hill* (17-C)	Chinese	415-648-9999	82	77	76
Ton Kiang–*Richmond* (40-C)	Chinese	415-386-8530	81	73	75
Aperto–*Potrero Hill* (28-C)	Italian/Mediterranean	415-252-1625	80	76	80
Bistro Clovis–*Civic Center* (18-M)	French	415-864-0231	80	74	76
Gira Polli–*North Beach* (14-C)	Italian	415-434-4102	79	76	80
LuLu Bis–*South of Market* (68-M)	French	415-495-5775	78	71	69
Zarzuela–*Russian Hill* (15-C)	Spanish	415-346-0800	76	69	71
Palio D'Asti–*Financial District* (14-M)	Italian	415-395-9800	76	69	68
Max's Diner–*South of Market* (48-C)	American	415-546-6297	75	74	75
Caffe Delle Stelle–*Civic Center* (36-C)	Italian	415-252-1110	75	69	75
Pane E Vino–*Pacific Heights* (23-C)	Italian	415-346-2111	75	70	71
Pizzeria Uno–*Marina* (22-C)	Pizza	415-563-3144	74	66	78
Mifune–*Japantown* (16-M)	Japanese	415-922-0337	74	65	77
Speckmann's–*Noe Valley* (14-C)	German	415-282-6850	73	66	72
David's–*Downtown* (17-VM)	Deli	415-771-1600	73	62	60
Delancy Street–*South of Market* (47-C)	American	415-512-5179	72	71	75
Des Alpes–*North Beach* (14-C)	Basque	415-391-4249	71	69	81
Capp's Corner–*North Beach* (22-C)	Italian	415-989-2589	71	65	77
Puccini & Pinetti–*Downtown* (14-M)	Italian	415-392-5500	71	71	67
Chevy's–*South of Market* (29-M)	Mexican	415-543-8060	70	70	70
Beach Chalet Brewery–*Golden Gate Park* (17-M)	Bistro	415-386-8439	70	70	68
Gordon Biersch–*South of Market* (30-C)	California	415-243-8246	70	64	64
Hamburger Mary's–*South of Market* (26-M)	American	415-626-5767	69	66	74
Chevy's–*Embarcadero* (18-M)	Mexican	415-391-2323	69	69	67
Cadillac Bar & Grill–*South of Market* (26-M)	Tex-Mex	415-543-8226	69	65	64
Cafe Claude–*Union Square* (23-M)	French	415-392-3505	68	64	67
Yet Wah–*Richmond* (14-M)	Chinese	415-387-8040	68	66	63
Olive Garden–*Stonestown* (31-VM)	Italian	415-661-6770	67	68	70

				Food	Service	Value

$$ *(continued)*

			Food	Service	Value
Bull's Texas Cafe–*Civic Center* (30-M)	Tex-Mex	415-864-4288	66	69	69
Patio Cafe–*Castro* (18-M)	California	415-621-4640	64	66	70
Lakeside Cafe–*Lakeside Village* (17-M)	American	415-337-0359	64	66	65
Don Ramon's–*South of Market* (13-C)	Mexican	415-864-2700	63	73	65

$$$

			Food	Service	Value
Helmand–*North Beach* (35-C)	Afghan	415-362-0641	87	77	85
Luzern–*Sunset* (29-C)	French/Swiss	415-664-2353	86	86	86
Scala's Bistro–*Union Square* (24-C)	Italian/French	415-395-8555	86	79	78
Vivande–*Pacific Heights* (21-C)	Italian	415-346-4430	86	80	75
Betelnut–*Marina* (18-C)	Asian	415-929-8855	85	80	78
Izzy's–*Marina* (22-C)	Steak	415-563-0487	84	77	76
Ristorante Bacco–*Noe Valley* (22-M)	Italian	415-282-4969	84	76	76
La Bergerie–*Richmond* (16-C)	French	415-387-3573	83	78	84
Laghi–*Richmond* (18-M)	Italian	415-386-6266	83	81	74
South Park Cafe–*South of Market* (32-C)	Bistro	415-495-7275	82	77	79
Cafe Riggio–*Richmond* (19-C)	Italian	415-221-2114	82	77	78
Moose's–*North Beach* (47-C)	California/Mediterranean	415-989-7800	82	79	74
Rumpus–*Union Square* (18-C)	California	415-421-2300	81	78	81
Pacific Cafe–*Richmond* (33-C)	Seafood	415-387-7091	81	78	79
Anjou–*Union Square* (20-C)	French	415-392-5373	81	80	78
Golden Turtle–*Pacific Heights* (14-C)	Vietnamese	415-441-4419	81	75	77
Garibaldi Cafe–*Potrero Hill* (27-C)	California	415-552-3325	81	78	77
Firefly–*Noe Valley* (20-C)	California	415-821-7652	81	79	74
Le Cyrano–*Richmond* (19-VM)	French	415-387-1090	80	74	81
Universal Cafe–*Potrero Flat* (14-VC)	California	415-821-4608	80	76	79
Straits Cafe–*Richmond* (20-C)	Singaporean	415-668-1783	80	76	78
Rose Pistola–*North Beach* (36-M)	Italian	415-399-0499	80	75	71
Ebisu–*Sunset* (25-M)	Japanese	415-566-1770	79	73	72
Bistro Roti–*South of Market* (35-C)	California/French	415-495-6500	79	75	71
Kuleto's–*Union Square* (53-C)	Italian	415-397-7720	79	72	70
Greens at Fort Mason–*Marina* (71-M)	Vegetarian	415-771-6222	79	72	70
Original Joe's–*Western Addition* (29-M)	Italian	415-775-4877	78	72	84
Ristorante Ecco–*South of Market* (21-C)	Italian	415-495-3291	78	76	76
Palomino–*South of Market* (40-C)	Mediterranean/Bistro	415-512-7400	78	79	76
Little City Antipasti Bar–*North Beach* (13-C)	Mediterranean	415-434-2900	78	74	76
Blue Muse–*Civic Center* (22-VC)	Continental	415-626-7505	78	74	72
Fog City Diner–*Embarcadero/N Beach* (38-C)	American	415-982-2000	78	76	72
Bizou–*South of Market* (31-C)	French	415-543-2222	78	77	72
City of Paris–*Union Square* (17-C)	Bistro	415-441-4442	77	76	79
Max's Opera Cafe–*Civic Center* (108-C)	American	415-771-7300	77	72	75
MacArthur Park–*Financial District* (30-VC)	American	415-398-5700	77	74	74
Ristorante Milano–*Russian Hill* (16-M)	Italian	415-673-2961	77	81	74
The Mandarin–*Ghirardelli Square* (16-VM)	Chinese	415-673-8812	77	77	71

$$$ *(continued)*

			Food	Service	Value
Sam's Grill–*Financial District* (33-M)	American	415-421-0594	77	71	70
Washington Sq Bar & Grill–*North Beach* (13-C)	American	415-982-8123	76	77	78
Tadich Grill–*Financial District* (50-VM)	American	415-391-1849	76	75	72
Cafe For All Seasons–*Twin Peaks* (37-M)	American	415-665-0900	76	72	71
Carta–*Central Market* (22-C)	Spanish	415-863-3516	76	70	69
Clement St Bar & Grill–*Richmond* (37-M)	California	415-386-2200	75	70	72
FAZ–*Financial District* (22-C)	Italian	415-362-0404	75	76	70
Stinking Rose–*North Beach* (25-M)	Italian	415-781-7673	75	71	67
Casa Aguila–*Sunset* (25-VM)	Mexican	415-661-5593	74	73	73
McCormick & Kuleto's–*Ghirardelli Sq* (35-M)	Seafood	415-929-1730	74	72	69
Il Fornaio–*Embarcadero* (40-M)	Italian	415-986-0100	74	70	68
Line-Up–*South of Market* (23-C)	Mexican	415-861-2887	73	77	76
Harbor Village–*Financial District* (27-M)	Chinese	415-781-8833	73	69	67
Fior d'Italia–*North Beach* (14-M)	Italian	415-986-1886	73	72	64
Upstairs at Cliff House–*Richmond* (32-M)	California	415-386-3330	72	73	68
Caffe Cozzolino–*Mission* (18-C)	Italian	415-285-6005	72	71	67
Bix–*Financial Dist/N Beach* (19-M)	American	415-433-6300	72	78	66
Courtyard–*Richmond* (20-C)	American	415-387-7616	70	74	74
Balboa Cafe–*Pacific Heights* (13-C)	California	415-921-3944	69	72	66
Villa D' Este–*Lakeside Village* (23-M)	Italian	415-334-0580	68	72	78
Empress of China–*Chinatown* (15-M)	Chinese	415-434-1345	68	63	64
Leticia's–*Upper Market* (17-M)	Mexican	415-621-0441	67	73	71
Schroeder's Cafe–*Financial District* (17-M)	German	415-421-4778	67	71	67

$$$$

			Food	Service	Value
The Terrace–Ritz-Carlton–*Nob Hill* (28-C)	Mediterranean	415-296-7465	92	91	82
Woodward's Garden–*Mission* (17-C)	California	415-621-7122	87	79	79
Postrio–*Union Square* (67-C)	California	415-776-7825	86	82	73
Cafe Kati–*Japantown* (23-M)	East-West	415-775-7313	85	79	74
Tommy Toy's–*Financial District* (26-C)	Chinese	415-397-4888	84	85	70
The Flying Saucer–*Mission* (17-C)	California	415-641-9955	83	74	79
Alfred's–*Financial District* (28-C)	Steak	415-781-7058	83	77	78
Splendido–*Financial District* (36-M)	Mediterranean	415-986-3222	83	80	76
House of Prime Rib–*Van Ness* (33-C)	Steak	415-885-4605	82	77	78
Boulevard–*Embarcadero* (86-M)	American	415-543-6084	82	77	71
Hong Kong Flower Lounge–*Richmond* (38-C)	Chinese	415-668-8998	81	69	75
Scoma's–*Fisherman's Wharf* (26-C)	Seafood	415-771-4383	81	76	70
Garibaldi's–*Pacific Heights* (17-VC)	Calif/Mediterranean	415-563-8841	80	79	77
Le Central–*Union Square* (16-M)	French	415-391-2233	80	84	73
Hayes Street Grill–*Civic Center* (65-M)	American	415-863-5545	78	75	70
Zuni Cafe & Grill–*Civic Center* (60-C)	Mediterranean	415-552-2522	78	66	67
Christophe–*Union Square* (18-VM)	California	415-771-6393	77	76	78
Cafe Majestic–*Civic Center* (15-M)	California	415-776-6400	77	80	68
Garden Court—Sheraton–*Fin District* (31-M)	Continental	415-392-8600	77	79	68

				Food	Service	Value

$$$$ *(continued)*

			Food	Service	Value
Stars–*Civic Center* (69-M)	California	415-861-7827	77	74	65
Brasserie Savoy–*Union Square* (29-C)	French	415-441-8080	76	74	71
Harry Denton's–*Embarcadero* (17-M)	American	415-882-1333	76	74	70
Scott's Seafood Grill–*Financial District* (35-M)	Seafood	415-981-0622	75	74	67
Wu Kong–*South of Market* (21-C)	Chinese	415-957-9300	73	72	65
L'Olivier–*Embarcadero/N. Beach* (13-M)	French	415-981-7824	73	74	64
PJ's Oyster Bed–*Sunset* (27-M)	Seafood	415-566-7775	72	70	69
Maye's Original Oyster Hse–*Russian Hill* (20-M)	Seafood	415-474-7674	71	67	68
Caffe Sport–*North Beach* (22-VM)	Italian	415-981-1251	70	55	56
Sinbad's Pier 2–*Embarcadero* (24-VM)	American	415-781-2555	67	70	67

$$$$$

			Food	Service	Value
Fleur de Lys–*Union Square* (41-C)	French	415-673-7779	90	82	73
Silks—Mandarin Hotel–*Financial District* (15-C)	Asian	415-986-2020	88	85	75
Masa's–*Union Square* (30-M)	French	415-989-7154	87	90	69
La Folie–*Russian Hill* (26-C)	French	415-776-5577	87	78	68
Campton Place–*Union Square* (30-M)	American	415-781-5555	83	85	69
Rubicon–*Financial District* (15-M)	French	415-434-4100	83	81	67
Hawthorne Lane–*South of Market* (39-C)	California	415-777-9779	82	82	69
French Room–*Theater District* (13-M)	French	415-775-4700	81	86	77
Carnelian Room–*Financial District* (34-M)	American	415-433-7500	81	83	72
Ruth's Chris Steak House–*Pacific Heights* (21-C)	Steak	415-673-0557	80	80	71
Harris'–*Pacific Heights* (44-M)	Steak	415-673-1888	80	78	69
Aqua–*Financial District* (55-M)	Seafood	415-956-9662	80	77	59
Cypress Club–*North Beach* (23-M)	California	415-296-8555	79	80	70
One Market–*Financial District* (39-M)	American	415-777-5577	79	77	70

SAN MATEO COUNTY

$

			Food	Service	Value
Applewood Inn–*Menlo Park* (18-M)	Pizza	650-324-3486	85	65	79
Jo Ann's Cafe–*S San Francisco* (33-C)	Breakfast/Lunch	650-872-2810	83	74	81
Brothers Delicatessen–*Burlingame* (38-M)	Deli	650-343-2311	74	71	76
Fresh Choice–*San Mateo* (29-M)	American	650-341-8498	70	67	76
Bakers Square–*Redwood City* (21-M)	American	650-367-8666	68	65	69

$$

			Food	Service	Value
Kabul–*San Carlos* (28-C)	Afghan	650-594-2840	81	81	81
Su Hong–*Menlo Park* (36-M)	Chinese	650-323-6852	81	73	79
Bertolucci's–*S San Francisco* (19-M)	Italian	650-588-1625	79	78	74
Pine Brook Inn–*Belmont* (43-C)	German	650-591-1735	77	78	78
Capellini Ristorante–*San Mateo* (48-M)	Italian	650-348-2296	77	69	70
La Pinata–*Burlingame* (13-M)	Mexican	650-375-1070	75	71	78
Celia's–*San Mateo* (19-M)	Mexican	650-343-5886	75	72	76
Amici's East Coast Pizzeria–*San Mateo* (14-VM)	Pizza	650-342-9392	75	73	66

					Food	Service	Value

$$ *(continued)*

Restaurant	Cuisine	Phone	Food	Service	Value
Lemon Tree–*Belmont* (20-C)	American	650-592-7273	74	73	74
Joe's of Westlake–*Daly City* (41-M)	Italian	650-755-7400	73	69	77
Chevy's–*Redwood City* (34-M)	Mexican	650-367-6892	72	73	72
Szechuan Flower–*San Mateo* (13-C)	Chinese	650-344-6831	72	75	68
Good Earth–*San Mateo* (34-VM)	California	650-349-0165	71	71	71
Chevy's–*Foster City* (17-C)	Mexican	650-572-8441	70	63	66
Buck's–*Woodside* (20-C)	American	650-851-8010	69	66	64
Pot Sticker–*San Mateo* (19-VC)	Chinese	650-349-0149	67	72	75
Chili's–*Menlo Park* (17-C)	Tex-Mex	650-321-0330	67	71	74
Lyon's–*San Mateo* (31-C)	American	650-349-5541	63	65	70
El Torito–*Daly City* (14-M)	Mexican	650-994-3210	62	66	69

$$$

Restaurant	Cuisine	Phone	Food	Service	Value
Buon Gusto–*S San Francisco* (15-M)	Italian	650-742-9777	86	83	73
20/30–*Redwood City* (34-C)	California/Mediterranean	650-363-2030	85	79	76
Mistral–*Redwood City* (17-C)	California/Mediterranean	650-802-9222	83	71	76
Iberia–*Portola Valley* (56-C)	Spanish	650-854-1746	83	73	73
Nina's Cafe–*Menlo Park* (13-C)	French	650-854-6386	82	72	71
Bogie's–*San Mateo* (25-M)	Continental	650-579-5911	82	76	71
Gaylord India–*Menlo Park* (21-C)	Indian	650-326-8761	81	75	71
Hungry Hunter–*S San Francisco* (15-C)	Steak	650-873-5131	80	76	73
Pasta Moon–*Half Moon Bay* (25-C)	Italian	650-726-5125	79	75	74
Basque Cultural Center–*S San Francisco* (33-C)	Basque	650-583-8091	78	75	82
Fontana's–*Menlo Park* (39-C)	Italian	650-321-0601	78	75	73
Carpaccio–*Menlo Park* (40-C)	Italian	650-322-1211	78	74	73
Woodside Bakery–*Woodside* (18-C)	Mediterranean	650-851-7247	78	74	68
Rico's Place–*San Carlos* (15-C)	Italian	650-592-7863	77	73	74
Max's Opera Cafe–*Burlingame* (51-M)	American	650-342-6297	77	75	73
Little Copenhagen–*Redwood City* (17-VM)	Danish	650-365-6616	77	68	72
Buffalo Grill–*San Mateo* (64-C)	American	650-358-8777	77	72	67
Max's–*Redwood City* (17-M)	American	650-365-6297	76	73	78
Duarte's Tavern–*Pescadero* (42-C)	Seafood	650-879-0464	76	70	73
Giglio's–*Foster City* (13-C)	Italian	650-341-1316	75	73	73
Moonraker–*Pacifica* (19-M)	American	650-359-0303	74	70	74
Fish Market–*San Mateo* (56-M)	Seafood	650-349-3474	74	71	72
The Acorn–*Menlo Park* (36-M)	Mediterranean	650-322-6201	74	72	70
Bayside Grill–*San Mateo* (18-C)	American	650-345-7844	74	74	68
Late for the Train–*Menlo Park* (27-C)	California	650-321-6124	73	70	69
Kuleto's–*Burlingame* (27-M)	Italian	650-342-4922	72	71	66
Black Angus–*Foster City* (45-C)	American	650-345-9971	71	70	71
Van's–*Belmont* (29-M)	American	650-591-6525	70	69	64
Barbara's Fish Trap–*Princeton-by-the-Sea* (27-C)	Seafood	650-728-7049	69	63	69
Nick's Rockaway–*Pacifica* (14-M)	American	650-359-3900	68	71	68
Woodlake Joe's–*San Mateo* (18-VM)	Italian	650-401-5637	68	67	67

$$$ *(continued)*

			Food	Service	Value
Fisherman–*Burlingame* (19-M)	Seafood	650-548-1490	67	70	64
Harbor House–*Redwood City* (15-C)	American	650-365-1386	63	56	64
Bobby McGee's–*Burlingame* (13-C)	American	650-579-7807	63	67	64

$$$$

			Food	Service	Value
231 Ellsworth–*San Mateo* (35-C)	French	650-347-7231	87	83	73
The Garden Grill–*Menlo Park* (13-C)	British	650-325-8981	84	75	69
Bella Vista–*Woodside* (27-VM)	Continental	650-851-1229	83	83	69
Hong Kong Flower Lounge–*Millbrae* (15-C)	Chinese	650-588-9972	82	71	71
Flea St Cafe–*Menlo Park* (40-C)	American	650-854-1226	81	80	72
Hong Kong Flower Lounge–*Millbrae* (39-C)	Chinese	650-878-8108	80	66	69
Shore Bird–*Princeton-by-the-Sea* (31-C)	American	650-728-5541	78	73	71
Gambardella's–*Menlo Park* (15-M)	Italian	650-325-6989	78	66	69
Village Pub–*Woodside* (19-C)	American	650-851-1294	78	75	68
Hyatt Hotel–*Burlingame* (14-C)	Italian	650-347-1234	78	65	64
Kincaid's–*Burlingame* (43-M)	American	650-342-9844	77	76	73
Le Pot au Feu–*Menlo Park* (17-M)	French	650-322-4343	74	72	71
Benihana of Tokyo–*Burlingame* (14-M)	Japanese	650-342-5202	73	73	65
Gulliver's–*Burlingame* (22-VM)	Steak	650-692-6060	72	74	68
Moss Beach Distillery–*Moss Beach* (19-M)	Seafood	650-728-5595	62	65	59

$$$$$

			Food	Service	Value
Iron Gate–*Belmont* (34-C)	Continental	650-592-7893	88	86	75
Dal Baffo–*Menlo Park* (40-C)	Continental	650-325-1588	88	85	67

SANTA CLARA/SANTA CRUZ/MONTEREY COUNTIES

$

			Food	Service	Value
Andale–*Palo Alto* (20-C)	Mexican	650-323-2939	81	73	83
Tony & Alba's–*Mountain View* (13-M)	Italian	650-968-5089	81	61	75
Andale–*Los Gatos* (16-C)	Mexican	408-395-8997	80	71	86
Pasand Madras Cuisine–*Santa Clara* (30-C)	Indian	408-241-5150	80	70	83
Hobee's–*San Jose* (14-C)	American	408-244-5212	80	71	81
Hobee's–*Palo Alto* (22-C)	American	650-856-6124	79	76	80
Fresh Choice–*Milpitas* (23-M)	American	408-262-6604	78	72	83
Fresh Choice–*Sunnyvale* (24-C)	American	408-732-7788	77	69	79
Hobee's–*Mountain View* (13-VM)	American	650-968-6050	77	74	76
Sweet Tomatoes–*Sunnyvale* (32-M)	American	408-730-8117	76	69	82
Fresh Choice–*San Jose* (18-M)	American	408-723-7991	76	68	76
Old Spaghetti Factory–*San Jose* (25-VM)	Italian	408-288-7488	73	68	86
Hobee's–*Palo Alto* (23-M)	American	650-327-4111	73	73	76
Fresh Choice–*Palo Alto* (57-M)	American	650-322-6995	72	68	81
Fresh Choice–*San Jose* (20-C)	American	408-866-1491	72	66	79

			Food	Service	Value
$$					
Kabul–*Sunnyvale* (32-C)	Afghan	408-245-4350	86	79	82
Sam's Bar-B-Que–*San Jose* (15-C)	BBQ	408-297-9151	83	79	82
La Fiesta–*Mountain View* (24-C)	Mexican	650-968-1364	83	77	82
Tao Tao Cafe–*Sunnyvale* (32-M)	Chinese	408-736-3731	80	68	72
Chef Chu's–*Los Altos* (72-M)	Chinese	650-948-2696	79	75	75
Osteria–*Palo Alto* (26-M)	Italian	650-328-5700	79	77	73
Piatti–*Palo Alto* (37-C)	Italian	650-324-9733	79	74	72
Armadillo Willy's BBQ–*Los Altos* (59-C)	BBQ	650-941-2922	78	74	76
Country Gourmet–*Sunnyvale* (26-M)	American	408-733-9446	78	62	73
Black Forest Inn–*Los Altos* (31-M)	German	650-948-8689	78	73	72
Good Earth–*Santa Clara* (13-C)	California	408-984-0960	77	74	76
Marie Callender's–*San Jose* (14-VC)	American	408-578-0643	76	76	80
Good Earth–*Cupertino* (39-M)	California	408-252-3555	75	74	74
Country Gourmet–*Mountain View* (25-C)	American	650-962-0239	75	70	74
Original Joe's–*San Jose* (52-M)	Italian	408-292-7030	75	73	74
Good Earth–*Los Gatos* (20-M)	California	408-395-6868	74	74	76
Fresco–*Palo Alto* (43-C)	American	650-493-3470	74	65	70
Spoons California Grill–*Campbell* (15-C)	American	408-559-7400	73	75	78
Su Hong–*Palo Alto* (26-M)	Chinese	650-493-3836	73	77	78
Marie Callender's–*San Jose* (20-C)	American	408-243-9018	73	71	76
Tied-House Cafe & Brewery–*San Jose* (19-C)	American	408-295-2739	73	70	72
Chevy's–*San Jose* (23-VM)	Mexican	408-266-1815	72	66	71
Coleman Still–*Santa Clara* (26-M)	Cajun	408-727-4670	71	68	75
Chili's–*San Jose* (22-M)	Tex-Mex	408-266-4800	71	70	73
Red Lobster–*San Jose* (14-VM)	Seafood	408-266-9275	71	72	72
Gordon Biersch–*Palo Alto* (20-M)	California	650-323-7723	71	68	69
Jing Jing–*Palo Alto* (15-VM)	Chinese	650-328-6885	71	66	67
Good Earth–*Palo Alto* (42-M)	California	650-321-9449	70	68	70
Ming's Villa–*East Palo Alto* (25-VM)	Chinese	650-856-7700	70	72	66
Olive Garden–*San Jose* (26-M)	Italian	408-225-1420	69	68	68
Tied-House Cafe & Brewery–*Mt View* (25-VM)	American	650-965-2739	68	66	70
Pedro's–*Santa Clara* (15-M)	Mexican	408-496-6777	68	67	69
Stickney's Hick'ry House–*Palo Alto* (22-VM)	American	408-324-0317	67	64	66
Chili's–*Cupertino* (16-C)	Tex-Mex	408-257-4664	66	70	70
Compadres Mexican Bar–*Palo Alto* (26-C)	Mexican	650-858-1141	66	68	69
Marie Callender's–*Los Altos* (21-C)	American	650-941-6990	66	69	67
Olive Garden–*Palo Alto* (27-M)	Italian	650-326-5673	65	68	68
Estrellita–*Los Altos* (13-VM)	Mexican	650-948-9865	62	61	62
$$$					
La Pastaia—De Anza Hotel–*San Jose* (29-M)	Italian	408-286-8686	84	79	74
Bistro Elan–*Palo Alto* (13-C)	Bistro	650-327-0284	84	77	73
Shadowbrook–*Capitola* (30-M)	California	408-475-1511	82	82	77
Mandarin Gourmet–*Palo Alto* (29-C)	Chinese	650-328-8898	82	78	72

$$$ *(continued)*

			Food	Service	Value
Eulipia–*San Jose* (29-C)	American	408-280-6161	82	77	70
Il Fornaio–*San Jose* (33-M)	Italian	408-271-3366	81	75	76
Henry's World Famous Hi-Life–*San Jose* (19-VM)	BBQ	408-295-5414	80	72	80
The Original Hick'ry Pit–*Campbell* (13-M)	BBQ	408-371-2400	79	75	77
Vahl's–*Alviso* (18-C)	Italian	408-262-0731	79	76	76
Babbo's–*Palo Alto* (20-C)	Mediterranean	650-321-1488	79	76	74
Bella Mia–*San Jose* (43-C)	Italian	408-280-1993	79	72	73
Ikenohana–*Cupertino* (14-M)	Japanese	408-252-6460	79	77	71
Frankie, Johnnie & Luigi–*Mountain View* (42-M)	Italian	650-967-5384	78	72	74
Fish Market–*Santa Clara* (47-M)	Seafood	408-246-3474	78	71	73
Fontana's–*Cupertino* (30-C)	Italian	408-725-0188	78	75	70
Hungry Hunter–*San Jose* (14-M)	Steak	408-266-3500	77	77	74
Tinnery–*Pacific Grove* (16-C)	American	408-646-1040	77	76	73
Il Fornaio–*Palo Alto* (87-M)	Italian	650-853-3888	77	70	68
Florentine–*Cupertino* (15-M)	Italian	650-253-6532	76	78	73
Florentine–*San Jose* (13-VM)	Italian	408-243-4040	76	77	73
Fish Market–*Palo Alto* (52-C)	Seafood	650-493-9188	76	71	73
Max's Opera Cafe–*Palo Alto* (57-M)	American	650-323-6297	75	71	72
Blue Sky Cafe–*Mountain View* (14-VM)	California	650-961-2082	75	70	71
Los Gatos Brewing Co–*Los Gatos* (22-C)	American	408-395-9929	75	74	69
Stuart Anderson's Black Angus–*Sunnyvale* (24-M)	Steak	408-245-4501	74	71	73
Stoddard's Brewhouse–*Sunnyvale* (21-M)	California	408-733-7824	74	69	68
Di Cicco's–*Campbell* (18-M)	Italian	408-377-5850	73	72	76
Black Angus–*San Jose* (23-M)	American	408-266-6602	73	70	72
Tony Roma's–*San Jose* (19-C)	California	408-253-4900	73	70	68
Lion and Compass–*Sunnyvale* (18-VM)	California	408-745-1260	73	69	63
Pacific Fresh–*Sunnyvale* (19-VM)	Seafood	408-745-1710	72	73	68
MacArthur Park–*Palo Alto* (37-C)	American	650-321-9990	72	69	65
Los Altos Bar & Grill–*Los Altos* (28-M)	American	650-948-4332	72	67	64
Teske's Germania–*San Jose* (19-M)	German	408-292-0291	71	71	65
Blue Chalk Cafe–*Palo Alto* (14-C)	American	650-326-1020	69	71	69
Hugo's–*Palo Alto* (13-M)	American	650-843-2521	68	67	64
Charley Brown's–*Sunnyvale* (29-C)	American	408-734-3460	68	64	63
Crow's Nest–*Santa Cruz* (20-M)	Seafood	408-476-4560	66	63	62

$$$$

			Food	Service	Value
Garden City–*San Jose* (23-C)	Continental	408-244-4443	88	78	75
Rue de Paris–*San Jose* (26-C)	French	408-298-0704	86	81	78
Eight Forty North First–*San Jose* (20-C)	American	408-282-0840	84	79	80
Paolo's–*San Jose* (32-C)	Italian	408-294-2558	84	80	70
Le Petit Bistro–*Mountain View* (21-M)	Bistro	650-964-3321	83	85	81
Evvia–*Palo Alto* (16-C)	Greek	650-326-0983	82	77	73
Bold Knight Cattleman's–*San Jose* (27-VC)	American	408-293-7700	81	79	82
Pigalle–*Los Gatos* (13-C)	French	408-395-7924	81	76	78

$$$$ *(continued)*

			Food	Service	Value
Three Flames–*San Jose* (19-C)	American	408-269-3133	80	78	82
Birk's–*Santa Clara* (28-C)	American	408-980-6400	80	79	70
Fuki Sushi–*Palo Alto* (19-C)	Japanese	650-494-9383	80	75	69
Nicolino's Garden Cafe–*Sunnyvale* (14-C)	Italian	408-734-5323	79	79	74
Lou's Village–*San Jose* (17-M)	Seafood	408-293-4570	78	75	75
California Cafe–*Palo Alto* (54-C)	California	650-325-2233	78	72	70
L'Amie Donia–*Palo Alto* (24-VM)	French	650-323-7614	78	73	69
Cafe Pro Bono–*Palo Alto* (34-M)	Italian	650-326-1626	77	78	72
Cafe Trio–*Los Gatos* (13-M)	California	408-356-8129	77	72	72
Beausejour–*Los Altos* (15-VM)	French	650-948-1382	77	76	68
Scott's Seafood Grill–*San Jose* (43-C)	Seafood	408-971-1700	77	76	67
Sundance Mine Co–*Palo Alto* (44-C)	Steak	650-321-6798	76	72	68
Scott's Seafood Grill–*Palo Alto* (33-C)	Seafood	650-856-1046	75	72	65
Maddalena's–*Palo Alto* (19-M)	Continental	650-326-6082	75	73	59
By-Th-Bucket–*Santa Clara* (16-C)	American	408-248-6244	73	69	67
Mac's Tea Room–*Los Altos* (41-C)	American	650-941-0234	72	73	70
Stars Palo Alto–*Palo Alto* (19-M)	American	650-321-4466	72	66	59
Palermo–*San Jose* (23-M)	Italian	408-297-0607	71	70	70
94th Aero-Squadron–*San Jose* (23-C)	American	408-287-6150	68	70	71

$$$$$

			Food	Service	Value
Le Papillon–*San Jose* (20-C)	French	408-296-3730	93	91	81
Emile's–*San Jose* (22-C)	French	408-289-1960	90	86	75
The Plumed Horse–*Saratoga* (17-C)	French	408-867-4711	87	87	74
Le Mouton Noir–*Saratoga* (27-M)	French	408-867-7017	86	82	73
Chez TJ–*Mountain View* (23-M)	French	650-964-7466	86	82	69
Chart House–*Los Gatos* (19-M)	American	408-354-1737	72	67	57

HOW TO USE THE RESTAURANT WRITE-UPS

Beginning on page 29, you'll find an alphabetical listing of the 259 higher rated restaurants, with information on each. Below is a single restaurant's listing, keyed to an explanation of each piece of information.

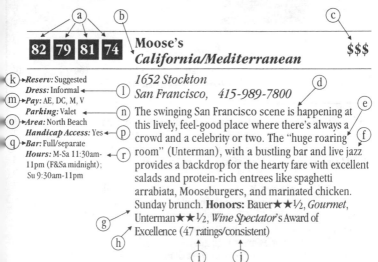

| 82 | 79 | 81 | 74 | **Moose's** *California/Mediterranean* | $$$ |

1652 Stockton
San Francisco,   415-989-7800

Reserv: Suggested
Dress: Informal
Pay: AE, DC, M, V
Parking: Valet
Area: North Beach
Handicap Access: Yes
Bar: Full/separate
Hours: M-Sa 11:30am-11pm (F&Sa midnight); Su 9:30am-11pm

The swinging San Francisco scene is happening at this lively, feel-good place where there's always a crowd and a celebrity or two. The "huge roaring room" (Unterman), with a bustling bar and live jazz provides a backdrop for the hearty fare with excellent salads and protein-rich entrees like spaghetti arrabiata, Mooseburgers, and marinated chicken. Sunday brunch. **Honors:** Bauer★★½, *Gourmet*, Unterman★★½, *Wine Spectator*'s Award of Excellence (47 ratings/consistent)

(a)   **Consumer ratings.** These are the average scores each restaurant received from subscribers to *CHECKBOOK* and *Consumer Reports* magazines who returned our questionnaires between 1994 and 1997 and reported having eaten there. The scores are for the quality of "food," "service," "ambience," and "value for your money." The ratings were converted to a scale that runs from 25 to 100. A score of 25 would mean that every rater considered the restaurant "unacceptable"; 100 would mean that every rater considered it "perfect." As a practical matter, the scores for food, for example, range from 58 to 94, with an average score of about 77. The key in using these ratings is to *compare* restaurants. The figure on the next page shows how restaurants' food scores were distributed among various categories.

Number of Restaurants by "Food" Rating Score

Food score

Food score	
90 or more	
85-89	
80 - 84	
75 - 79	
70 -74	
65 - 69	
Below 65	

0   40   80   120   160   200
Number of restaurants

(b)   **Cuisine.** We've categorized a restaurant's cuisine based on management's own claims and our review of menus. Many restaurants offer a variety of types of cooking and so aren't easily categorized, but our description should give you a rough idea of what to expect.

(c)   **Price category.** We've categorized restaurants on the basis of the average cost of dinner *entrees*, exclusive of tax, tip, and such items as appetizers, beverages, and desserts. The figure on the next page shows what the categories are and the number of restaurants that fell within each.

These categories are rough guides at best. For example, a restaurant in the "$$" category ($9.01 to $13) might well offer a few entrees for well below $9 and others costing considerably more than $13. Also, remember that your total *meal* will cost more than these *entree* price ranges. Tax and tip alone will add more than 20 percent, and you are very likely to have drinks, an appetizer, a dessert, or some other item that adds to the cost. Often the extras are relatively more expensive than the basic entree. Finally, there has to be an element of judgment in our price groupings. For example, we had to adjust figures for restaurants that charge by the several-course dinner and don't price by entree alone; and if a restaurant's entrees automatically include appetizer, dessert, and beverage, we adjusted down the entree price when assigning the restaurant to a price category.

(d)   **Description.** One element of each restaurant's write-up is a few comments on the type of food served, the nature of the service, and the ambience. We also mention especially popular or appealing menu items. This information is based on our own knowledge of the restaurants, questionnaires and interviews completed by restaurant management, menus and other written materials supplied by the restaurants, published reviews, and most important, thousands of comments made by our consumer raters.

(e)   **Professional reviewers' comments.** For comparison, we've tried to pull out key phrases that highlight the insights, judgments, or recommendations of professionals who have reviewed the restaurant. Many of the restaurants, however, have not been reviewed, and even for those that have, our selected phrases capture only a fragment of the entire review, although we've tried to retain the reviewer's intent.

To obtain this information, we gathered reviews from local newspapers and magazines from January 1997 to August 1998: the *Contra Costa Times*, the *Oakland Tribune*, the *San Francisco Chronicle*, the *San Francisco Examiner*, the *San Jose Mercury News*, and *Gourmet* magazine. To distinguish them from one another, we have listed the reviewers' last names instead of referring to the publications where they appear. Reviewers for the *Contra Costa Times*: Nicholas Boer, Deborah Byrd, Maggie Crum, Carol Fowler, Ken Miller, Lisa Wrenn; for the *San Francisco Chronicle*: Michael Bauer, Maria Cianci, Robin Davis, Laura Hamburg, Miriam Morgan, Karola Saekel; for the *San Francisco Examiner*: Patricia

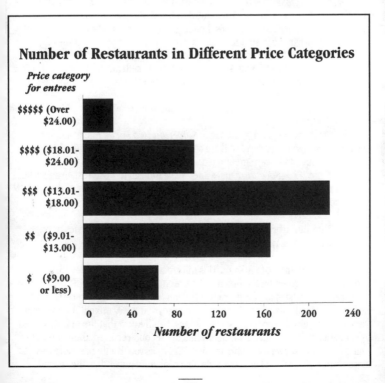

Number of Restaurants in Different Price Categories

Price category for entrees

Number of restaurants

Unterman; and for the *San Jose Mercury News*: Sheila Himmel. Remarks in quotes without any identification are comments from our raters.

(f)   **Entertainment.** We note whether a restaurant offers entertainment and very briefly describe it. In many cases, this entertainment is quite modest—an occasional pass through by a guitarist, for example. Moreover, entertainment arrangements change constantly. If you're interested, call before going and find out what's on schedule, when it will occur, and whether there is a cover charge.

(g)   **Cross references to other restaurant locations** *(none for sample restaurant)*. If a restaurant has other locations that appear on the Quick-Check Table beginning on page 8, we tell you here. We've usually included a write-up in the alphabetical listing only for the location with the highest food score. (Several restaurants had high enough consumer ratings scores to be included in our alphabetical listing but are not among the 259 listed only because another location of the same restaurant was listed.)

(h)   **Honors.** To provide a point of comparison with the scores of our raters, we've reported honors received by any restaurant that has been rated in the *Contra Costa Times*, *Oakland Tribune*, *San Francisco Chronicle*, *San Francisco Examiner*, and *San Jose Mercury News* between January 1997 and August 1998. Once again we've used the names of individual reviewers to identify who has given the honor. Four stars are the highest honor given by every newspaper. The *Contra Costa Times* originally used a four star system but now offers two grades for each restaurant, the first for "food" and the second for "ambience/service;" possible grades range from A to D, with A=Exceptional, B=Excellent, C=Good, and D=Fair.
    We've also reported on the following honors for any restaurant that has earned them.
    Restaurants reviewed by *Gourmet* magazine from January 1997 to August 1998 are mentioned here.
    From the August 1998 issue of *San Francisco Focus* magazine, restaurants named in its readers' poll are specified along with the name of the category in which they were mentioned.
    From *Wine Spectator* magazine, we've indicated those restaurants whose wine list received a "Grand Award," "Award of Excellence," or "Best of Award of Excellence"as reported in the September 30, 1998 issue.

(i)   **Number of ratings.** This is the number of survey responses upon which our consumer ratings scores are based.

(j)   **Consistency of ratings.** This information tells you the degree to which different raters agreed on the quality of the restaurant (the degree of consistency we've reported relates to "food" ratings). If you're considering two restaurants, each with a "food" score of 75, and the first received "very mixed" ratings while the second received "very consistent" ratings, you'll know that the first was loved by some raters and disliked by others while the second received about an average rating from almost everyone who ate there. This tells you that there's more risk and more chance of a real treat in going to the first restaurant rather than the second.

The consistency information, when combined with information on the number of consumer ratings, also bears on a second point: the confidence you can put in the ratings.

The consumer ratings are obviously an imperfect measure. For example, some restaurants may have scored low just because they were rated by unusually critical raters or because the raters hit them on a bad day or ordered the worst items on the menu. The risk of such distortions is lower if there are a large number of raters and consistent ratings than if the opposite is true. The table below gives you an idea of the size of the differences in score you should look for in deciding whether the difference between two restaurants is important. For example, if both restaurants were rated by 30 raters and both received "consistent" ratings, you wouldn't want to put much weight on a difference in the two restaurants' scores unless one restaurant's score was at least five points higher than the other's.

Remember that even consistent large differences in the ratings two restaurants receive from large numbers of raters won't mean much if different types of individuals, with different standards or biases, rated the different restaurants. And remember that even if all of our raters loved a restaurant, that's no assurance that your tastes will run along the same lines.

(k)   **Reservations.** We've reported the restaurant's most stringent policy regarding reservations at dinner for small parties (up to six people) and the days it applies if not every day. The policy for lunch is reported if it is more stringent than the policy for dinner. Many restaurants require reservations at lunch and dinner for parties of six or more. Our categories are "Required," "Accepted," "Suggested," and "Not Accepted."

How Many Points Difference in Ratings Score You Should Look For in Comparing Two Restaurants

Consistency category	Number of ratings for each of two restaurants you are comparing			
	13	30	60	100
Very consistent	5	3	2	2
Consistent	8	5	3	3
Mixed	11	7	5	4
Very mixed	14	9	6	5

(l)   **Dress.** This is the restaurant's most stringent dress requirement for male patrons at dinner and the days it applies if not every day. The dress code for lunch is reported if it is more stringent than the one for dinner. Our categories are "Coat [and/or] Tie Required," "Coat [and/or] Tie Suggested," "Informal."

(m)   **Payment.** Accepted forms of payment are reported here: cash only, personal checks, and the following credit cards—AE (American Express), DC (Diners Club), Disc (Discover), M (MasterCard), and V (Visa). Those restaurants that accept personal checks often require one or more major credit cards for identification. U.S. traveler's checks are assumed to be acceptable everywhere.

(n)   **Parking.** This refers to the availability of free parking in a restaurant lot or a public lot. Categories are "Yes," "No," "Valet" (includes "Yes" unless otherwise noted). For some restaurants, parking conditions apply only at certain times, and we have included that information when available. For example, "Yes after 6pm" indicates that free or validated parking is available in a public lot or parking garage after 6pm. Of course, at some restaurants that don't offer lot parking, parking will be no problem for you—if there is ample parking on the street.

(o)   **Area.** Commonly used area or neighborhood names are reported to help you locate the restaurant.

(p)   **Handicap Access.** The information on access for handicapped persons was obtained largely from the restaurants themselves. We did not inspect the restaurants to determine the extent to which they met established standards for handicapped access. Secondary sources that report accessibility based on on-site inspections were used to verify the restaurants' reports to the maximum extent possible. The categories used are "Yes," "No," and "Limited." If a restaurant said it was not accessible, we took its word on the matter. "Limited" usually indicates that the parking or restroom facilities do not meet the standards for handicapped access. Handicapped persons should interpret the information reported here only as a general indicator of accessibility, not as a guarantee. We hope it will be helpful, but we suggest you call the restaurant before going.

(q)   **Bar.** We indicate here what type of alcoholic beverages are served— "Wine," "Beer," "Full" (meaning cocktails in addition to wine and beer), or "None." We also include the word "Separate" when you can get drinks not just at your table but also at a separate bar.

(r)   **Hours.** Approximate opening and closing times for the dining room are reported. But keep in mind that this information is hard to pin down and changes frequently. The hours reported are the approximate hours during which food is served; many restaurants have lounge areas that remain open after the dining room is closed, but we have not reported those variations. Again, if this information is of particular importance to you, we suggest you call and verify the hours for the day in question.

Food	Service	Ambience	Value

| 72 | 73 | 69 | 77 |

Abernathy's $$
American

Reserv: Suggested
Dress: Informal
Pay: AE, DC, M, V, Checks
Parking: Yes
Handicap Access: Ltd
Bar: Full/separate
Hours: Daily 11am-3pm,
5-9pm (F&Sa 10pm)

1411 Locust
Walnut Creek   925-934-9490

There are two reasons why this restaurant/club maintains its place on the local roadmap. One is that it hosts live music nightly. Second, you'll find a bevy of good drinking and dining values if you play your cards right. Bargain lunch buffets precede later afternoon happy hour specials served with the popular early bird dinners. The full menu offers meals of yesteryear like steak, ribs, and seafood, served in the dark, clubby atmosphere. Outdoor dining. (23 ratings/consistent)

| 84 | 80 | 76 | 80 |

Ajanta $$
Indian

Reserv: Accepted
Dress: Informal
Pay: AE, DC, Disc, M, V, Checks
Handicap Access: Ltd
Bar: Beer/wine
Hours: Daily 11:30am-2:30pm;
5:30-9:30 pm

1888 Solano Ave
Berkeley   510-526-4373

A haven for the tandoori/curry crowd, this place "is packed night after night" due to the changing and fixed-price menus of diverse, exotic specialties that "show the depth of (chef-owner) Moorjani's cooking skills" (Davis). Look for tandoori fish, braised lamb, and sea bass in yogurt. Unusual murals depicting caves in Ajanta add an element of intrigue to the refined setting. Service is friendly and personalized. **Honors:** Davis★★½
(28 ratings/consistent)

| 83 | 77 | 76 | 78 |

Alfred's $$$$
Steak

Reserv: Suggested
Dress: Informal
Pay: AE, M, V
Parking: Valet only (5:30-10pm)
Area: Financial District
Handicap Access: Yes
Bar: Full
Hours: M-F 11:30am-10pm;
Sa&Su 5-10pm

659 Merchant St
San Francisco   415-781-7058

There's no lack of Old World charm in this ballroom setting with glittering chandeliers, upholstered booths, and deep red accents. Here you'll find the "best steak in town," like the porterhouse (called "the King") that weighs 32 ounces and "great martinis" (Crum). For a "blast from the past" (Bauer) try the antipasto platter, real Caesar salad, or fried cream that's "rich and full of calories" (Crum). Outdoor dining. **Honors:** Bauer★★½, Crum B/B (28 ratings/consistent)

80 71 69 86   Andale $
Mexican

Reserv: Not accepted
Dress: Informal
Pay: Cash Only
Parking: No
Handicap Access: Yes
Bar: Beer/wine
Hours: M-F 11am-10pm;
Sa&Su 9am-9pm (Sa 10pm)

21 N Santa Cruz Ave
Los Gatos   408-395-8997

Tired of paying too much and getting too little? More than a decade old, this fresh-Mex taqueria offers values galore if you like specialties from Jalisco like soft tacos, burritos, or chicken tamales. For tried-and-true chili heads try the Yucateco salsa de habanero, but leave your tuxedo at home—this is tasty fast food. It's simple, cheap, and satisfying. Weekend brunch. Outdoor dining. See Quick-Check Table for highly-rated Palo Alto location. (16 ratings/consistent)

82 81 75 81   Angkor Wat $$
Cambodian

Reserv: Suggested
Dress: Informal
Pay: AE, M, V
Parking: No
Area: Richmond
Handicap Access: Yes
Bar: Full/separate
Hours: M-Sa 11am-2:30pm;
Daily 5-10:30pm

4217 Geary Blvd
San Francisco   415-221-7887

Heralded as the most aromatic Cambodian food in the Bay Area, raters praise the food, reasonable prices, and striking decor with its wall murals, garden courtyard, and cushioned floor seating. Live weekend performances by the Cambodian Ballet and a friendly owner add to the amenities. Good for groups when you can order and share several things like Cambodian crepe, chicken-lemongrass soup, five-spice shark, green papaya salad, or duck curry. (27 ratings/consistent)

81 80 82 78   Anjou $$$
French

Reserv: Suggested
Dress: Informal
Pay: AE, DC, Disc, M, V
Parking: No
Area: Union Square
Handicap Access: Ltd
Bar: Full
Hours: Tu-Sa 11:30am-
2:30pm, 5:30-10pm

44 Campton Pl
San Francisco   415-392-5373

The decor is très chic right down to the artwork, exposed brick walls, and brass railings at this cozy alley bistro that's oh so French and not too noisy. Here you'll find classic brasserie fare with a few nuances like grilled steak and pommes frites, cassoulet, and tarte Tatin alongside roasted quail and lots of good values including the three-course lunch that raters term "a real deal." Service is warm and friendly. Outdoor dining. (20 ratings/consistent)

Food **Service** **Ambience** **Value**

| 80 | 76 | 68 | 80 |

Aperto $$
Italian/Mediterranean

Reserv: Not accepted
Dress: Informal
Pay: AE, DC, M, V, Checks
Parking: No
Area: Potrero Hill
Handicap Access: Yes
Bar: Beer/wine
Hours: M-F 11:30am-2:30pm, 5:30pm-10pm; Sa 11am-2:30pm, 5:30-10pm; Su 10am-2:30pm, 5-9pm

1434 18th St
San Francisco 415-252-1625

A local hangout that's packed, noisy, and cramped, yet raters say "is almost too good to be just a neighborhood place." No reservations are taken, so expect a wait while you inhale the great aromas emanating from the kitchen. Smooth and unpretentious staff shuttle plates mounded with rustic specialties like mushroom pasta, roasted chicken, house-cured pork chops, and chocolate soufflé cake. Portions are generous; prices are low. Weekend brunch. (28 ratings/consistent)

| 85 | 65 | 60 | 79 |

Applewood Inn $
Pizza

Reserv: Not accepted
Dress: Informal
Pay: AE, Disc, M, V, Checks
Parking: No
Handicap Access: Yes
Bar: Beer/wine
Hours: Daily 5-10pm (Su 9pm)

1001 El Camino Real
Menlo Park 650-324-3486

It's clearly not the minimalist Bavarian decor or window counter service on which the legacy of this spot has been built, it's the 17 types of pizzas—some usual, some not so usual, like smoked salmon, sauerkraut, or Hungarian sausage that raters can't stop raving about. Everyone seems to have their own favorite, but almost all lament that the place needs more tables; the best advice is to do take out and find a seat elsewhere. (18 ratings/mixed)

| 80 | 77 | 80 | 59 |

Aqua $$$$$
Seafood

Reserv: Suggested
Dress: Coat/tie suggested
Pay: AE, DC, M, V
Parking: Valet only (dinner)
Area: Financial District
Handicap Access: Yes
Bar: Full
Hours: M-F 11:30am-2:30pm, 5:30-10:30pm; Sa 5:30-10:30pm

252 California St
San Francisco 415-956-9662

The critics may swoon about the "dramatic lighting, high ceilings, wonderful art and the most beautiful flower arrangements in the city" (Bauer), but our raters seem to know a bad value when they see it. Those with ample pocketbooks may have expectations fulfilled with the trend-setting food such as house specialties of mussel soufflé, scallops, sole, and desserts. Daily prix fixe menus. **Honors:** Bauer★★★, *Wine Spectator*'s Award of Excellence (55 ratings/mixed)

Food	Service	Ambience	Value

78	74	68	76

Armadillo Willy's BBQ
BBQ $$

Reserv: Not accepted
Dress: Informal
Pay: AE, M, V
Parking: Yes
Handicap Access: Yes
Bar: Beer/wine/margaritas
Hours: M-F 11am-10pm;
Sa&Su noon-10pm (Su 9:30pm)

1031 N San Antonio Rd
Los Altos   650-941-2922

"This is Texas BBQ!" with a back-shed atmosphere and it's sweeping the area by storm. Rustle up a plate of award-winning ribs, top-notch fajitas, slow-cooked brisket, or BBQ chicken with some peanut slaw and cornbread on the side. A children's menu and crayons on the table make it a great place for kids, though some say takeout's your best bet during peak hours. Either way, you can still buy a Willy's T-shirt to show the folks at home. (59 ratings/consistent)

85	85	93	73

Auberge du Soleil
California $$$$$

Reserv: Suggested
Dress: Informal
Pay: AE, DC, Disc, M, V
Parking: Valet
Handicap Access: Yes
Bar: Full
Hours: Daily 7-11am, 11:30am-2:30pm, 6-9:30pm (Sa&Su 5:30-9:30pm)

180 Rutherford Hill Rd
Rutherford   707-967-3111

Dining al fresco you'll find fabulous vineyard views from the wisteria-covered deck, while inside, rustic half-timbered ceilings, open fireplaces, and earth-toned walls set the mood for the eclectic menu and ample wine list that draws from all corners of the earth. Raters say it's one of the most beautiful destination spots than can be found when you're in the mood for a country outing and have money to spare. **Honors:** *Wine Spectator*'s Best of Award of Excellence (28 ratings/mixed)

73	73	64	75

Back Forty Texas BBQ
BBQ $$

Reserv: Accepted
Dress: Informal
Pay: AE, Disc, M, V
Parking: Yes
Handicap Access: Yes
Bar: Full
Hours: Daily 11am-9pm

1918 Oak Park Blvd
Pleasant Hill   925-935-1440

It's not an ordinary 'cue joint when the National Rib Cookoff proclaims your BBQ sauce the best in the country. It's the perfect foil for their chicken, pork and beef ribs that are a meal in themselves, and of course, the Forty's classic homemade links. So jus' set yourself down, take in the big screens or rustic tack hanging around, and order a microbrew on tap for a comfortable evening out. (44 ratings/consistent)

| Food | Service | Ambience | Value |

| 72 | 74 | 64 | 85 |

Banchero's $
Italian

Reserv: Suggested
Dress: Informal
Pay: AE, M, V
Parking: Yes
Handicap Access: Yes
Bar: Full
Hours: Tu-F 4-9pm
(F 9:30pm); Sa 3-9:30pm;
Su 12:30-9pm

20102 Mission Blvd
Hayward   510-276-7355

Need something uplifting after your April 15 tax dead-line? Try this grandfather of family-style eateries whose philosophy is "more is better" and diners almost always leave with huge doggie bags that will carry them well into the next day and beyond. House favorites like fried chicken, rib eye steak, and cutlets a la parmigiana come with several courses at prices you won't believe. Great for families, group outings, and seniors. Expect a wait. (28 ratings/consistent)

| 87 | 83 | 82 | 74 |

Barone's $$$
Continental

Reserv: Suggested
Dress: Informal
Pay: AE, DC, Disc, M, V
Parking: Yes
Handicap Access: Yes
Bar: Full/separate
Hours: M-F 11:30am-2:30pm,
5:30-9:30pm (F 10pm);
Sa 5:30-10pm; Su 5-9pm

475 St John St
Pleasanton   925-426-0987

Graceful, refined dining awaits you in this tastefully updated Victorian that receives accolades for its food and service. Start your meal with an order of scoozi flatbread and proceed on to their top-notch seafood, pastas, salads, and specialties from the grill. There's al fresco dining when the weather permits, or an enclosed sun porch for cooler temperatures, and on weekends, live piano music in the bar. Good selection of wines. (19 ratings/consistent)

| 78 | 75 | 70 | 82 |

Basque Cultural Center $$$
Basque

Reserv: Suggested
Dress: Informal
Pay: AE, DC, M, V
Parking: Yes
Handicap Access: Yes
Bar: Full/separate
Hours: Tu-F 11:30am-2:30pm,
5:30-9:30pm; Sa 5:30-9:30pm;
Su 5-9pm

599 Railroad Ave
S San Francisco   650-583-8091

Authentic family recipes from the Pyrenees team up with huge portions, friendly service, and low prices at this boisterous gathering spot for displaced Basques. Menu options include family-style multi-course meals with huge tureens of soup and several courses of honest comfort food like oxtail stew, lamb, or basque-style salmon. A la carte items include superb rack of lamb or tangy pepper steak. Often crowded and noisy. (33 ratings/consistent)

| Food | Service | Ambience | Value |

82 **74** **75** **77**

Bay View Restaurant
Continental
$$$$

Reserv: Suggested
Dress: Coat/tie suggested
Pay: AE, Disc, M, V
Parking: Yes
Handicap Access: Yes
Bar: Full/separate
Hours: W-Su 5-10pm
(Sa 11pm)

800 Coast Hwy
Bodega Bay 707-875-2751

The seafood is always dependable at this local wharfside favorite where you can watch the fishing boats bring in their catch that'll soon end up in the kitchen. High marks go not only to the king salmon, but the rack of lamb and filet mignon. For special twilight dining, come on Saturday when live piano music is featured, otherwise enjoy the lovely bay vistas during daylight hours. (16 ratings/very consistent)

82 **80** **77** **75**

Bay Wolf
Mediterranean
$$$

Reserv: Suggested
Dress: Informal
Pay: M, V, Checks
Parking: No
Handicap Access: Ltd
Bar: Beer/wine
Hours: M-F 11:30am-2pm,
6-9:30pm; Sa&Su 5:30-9:30pm

3853 Piedmont Ave
Oakland 510-655-6004

"Duck has become a star" at this creative California-style pioneer that has dished "up delicious food for decades without much fanfare" (Bauer). The seasonal menu offered in this attractive Victorian home changes often, but always offers duck flan that's "one of the best appetizers I can remember" (Bauer). Expect unobtrusive service in the romantic craftsman setting with pleasant al fresco dining. **Honors:** Bauer★★★, Boer A-/A (76 ratings/mixed)

83 **83** **87** **69**

Bella Vista
Continental
$$$$

Reserv: Suggested
Dress: Informal
Pay: AE, DC, Disc, M, V
Parking: Yes
Handicap Access: Yes
Bar: Full/separate
Hours: M-Sa 5-9pm (F&Sa
10pm)

13451 Skyline Blvd
Woodside 650-851-1229

Looking for something romantic and worthy of a special occasion? The vistas at this woodsy mountaintop retreat are especially beautiful at night with the glittering lights of the South Bay below. A crackling fire inside pairs up with refined service and continental cuisine that harks back to the days of grandeur. House specials include La Liaison Bella Vista (surf and turf) and dishes prepared tableside that are expensive, but for the view, worth it. (27 ratings/very mixed)

Food	Service	Ambience	Value

85 **80** **81** **78**

Betelnut
Asian $$$

Reserv: Suggested
Dress: Informal
Pay: DC, Disc, M, V
Parking: Yes
Area: Marina
Handicap Access: Yes
Bar: Full
Hours: Su-Th 11:30am-11pm;
F&Sa 11:30am-midnight

2030 Union
San Francisco   415-929-8855

The teaming of a pan-Asian specialties and small plates menu with east and west brews at this Asian beer house has caused a stir in the local dining scene. The mood is "sensual and slightly clandestine" (Bauer) with lacquered red walls, bamboo fans, and filtered amber lighting, punctuated by bustling sidewalk tables and a lively bar. Look for the sundried anchovies, smoked sea bass, Singapore crab, and Korean pork. Good for groups. **Honors:** Bauer★★ (18 ratings/consistent)

80 **79** **71** **70**

Birk's
American $$$$

Reserv: Suggested
Dress: Informal
Pay: AE, DC, Disc, M, V
Parking: Yes
Area: Silicon Valley
Handicap Access: Yes
Bar: Full/separate
Hours: M-F 11:15am-2:30pm,
5-10pm; Sa&Su 5-10pm

3955 Freedom Cir
Santa Clara   408-980-6400

A power lunch hangout that has etched its name in the annals of Silicon Valley for its slick, upscale bistro atmosphere, tasty pastas, impressive wine offerings, and excellent grilled specialties. Best of the lot are the steaks and ribs or the smoked prime rib on weekends. A number of small plates are tailored for light eating. The amply stocked bar has a large assortment of beers on tap and single malts. The only complaint is the noise when it's crowded. **Honors:** Himmel★★★ (28 ratings/consistent)

80 **74** **68** **76**

Bistro Clovis
French $$

Reserv: Suggested
Dress: Informal
Pay: AE, DC, Disc, M, V
Parking: No
Area: Civic Center
Handicap Access: Yes
Bar: Beer/wine
Hours: M 11:30am-2:30pm;
Tu-Sa 11:30am-2:30pm, 5:30-
10pm (F&Sa 11pm)

1596 Market St
San Francisco   415-864-0231

A true bistro/wine bar that offers classics like onion soup, lamb salad, sweetbreads, seafood casserole, and incredible tarte Tatin in charming but cramped quarters complete with lace curtains, cafe chairs, and wood floors. Daily tastings of three similar wines from various regions of France are available for those who want to explore. Close to the symphony and opera, raters advise reserving ahead for "one of the best light meals around." (18 ratings/mixed)

Food	Service	Ambience	Value		
84	**77**	**73**	**73**	**Bistro Elan** *Bistro*	**$$$**

Reserv: Suggested
Dress: Informal
Pay: AE, DC, M, V
Parking: No
Handicap Access: Yes
Bar: Beer/wine
Hours: Tu-F 11:30am-2pm,
5:30-10pm; Sa 5:30-10pm

448 California Ave
Palo Alto   650-327-0284

The ubiquitous bistro decor, with a hammered tin bar, butter-colored walls, casual cafe tables, and al fresco patio dining amidst flowering herbs, pairs up with a small but carefully chosen menu at this popular and lively neighborhood place. House favorites include poached egg on brioche with Sevruga caviar, grilled rib eye steak with pommes frites, and pan-seared salmon with root vegetables. Though sometimes noisy, it's still friendly and casual. (13 ratings/consistent)

74	**68**	**67**	**81**	**The Blue Nile** *Ethiopian*	**$**

Reserv: Suggested weekends
Dress: Informal
Pay: M, V
Parking: No
Handicap Access: Yes
Bar: Beer/wine
Hours: Tu-Sa 11:30am-10pm;
Su 5-10pm

2525 Telegraph Ave
Berkeley   510-540-6777

Finger food reaches new heights at this local favorite where diners eat authentically—without utensils. Portions are large, prices low, and the food intriguing, although some give it mixed reviews for mediocre service and ambience. Main course highlights include ye doro tibs (simmered chicken), the Nile veggie combo platter, and kitfo (spiced beef). Good place for groups to sample and share and still have money to spare. (17 ratings/mixed)

82	**76**	**79**	**71**	**Bogie's** *Continental*	**$$$**

Reserv: Required
Dress: Informal
Pay: AE, DC, M, V, Checks
Parking: No
Handicap Access: Yes
Bar: Full/separate
Hours: Tu-F 11:30am-2:30pm,
5-10pm; Sa&Su 5-10pm

60 East Third Ave
San Mateo   650-579-5911

A date in Casablanca comes alive at this romantic hideaway that's filled with '40's nostalgia. The Maltese falcon perches over the movie memorabilia, Hollywood posters, and dining tables festooned with pink linens and roses. The menu looks like it would have in Bogie's era: beef fillet, rack of lamb, Royal wiener schnitzel. The elegant prices left some raters wondering whether they'll play it again. Nonetheless, gypsy music (Tu) and the unique setting make it a fun place. (25 ratings/mixed)

Food **Service** **Ambience** **Value**

| 81 | 79 | 69 | 82 |

Bold Knight Cattleman's
American $$$$

Reserv: Not accepted
Dress: Informal
Pay: AE, DC, M, V, Checks
Parking: Yes
Handicap Access: Yes
Hours: M-F 11am-2pm, 5-10pm (F 11pm); Sa 5-11pm; Su 1-10pm

1600 Monterey Rd
San Jose   408-293-7700

Some restaurants never change and this is one of them. Most who come here start out with the cheese fondue, proceed to thick slabs of beef served with baked potatoes, then cap it all off with a wedge of homemade pie. The lounge-like setting with leatherette booths is perfect for settling in for a significant meal while you're entertained by a live singer (Wednesday to Sunday). For those who want it less formal, there's a coffee shop next door that's open late. (27 ratings/very consistent)

| 78 | 71 | 78 | 78 |

Boran Thai
Thai $

Reserv: Accepted
Dress: Informal
Pay: Disc, M, V
Parking: No
Handicap Access: Yes
Bar: Beer/wine
Hours: M-Sa 11:30am-10pm; Su 4pm-9:30pm

1892 Solano Ave
Berkeley   510-525-3625

This family-run operation is known for its consistently fresh and tasty meals, large portions, and low prices. The menu features a large selection of both vegetarian and non-vegetarian entrees. Favorites include Thai egg rolls, calamari or beef sald, red chicken curry, vegetarian special, and coconut ice cream. Carved wood panels, cushioned floor seating, and intimate temple-like dining areas add an exotic note to the attractive setting. (14 ratings/very consistent)

| 82 | 77 | 81 | 71 |

Boulevard
American $$$$

Reserv: Required
Dress: Informal
Pay: AE, DC, Disc, M, V
Parking: Valet only
Area: Embarcadero
Handicap Access: Yes
Bar: Full/separate
Hours: M-F 11:30am-2:15pm, 5:30-10pm (Th&F 10:30pm); Sa&Su 5:30-10:30pm (Su 10pm)

One Mission St (at Steuart)
San Francisco   415-543-6084

Considered by many to be "the belle of the ball," this mega-bistro has been a huge success since it opened. And for good reasons: it sports stunning decor, has sweeping views in a happening locale, and continues to dazzle many with its fabulous cutting-edge menu that changes daily. Some dissidents grumble about uneven quality and high prices, but most give it the high five. **Honors:** *Focus* Best and Best San Francisco Area, *Wine Spectator*'s Award of Excellence (86 ratings/mixed)

| Food | Service | Ambience | Value |

78 77 76 76

Brava Terrace
California $$$

Reserv: Suggested
Dress: Informal
Pay: AE, DC, Disc, M, V
Parking: Yes
Handicap Access: Yes
Bar: Full/separate
Hours: Daily noon-9pm
(closed W Nov-April)

3010 St Helena Hwy N
St Helena   707-963-9300

One of the first local chefs to migrate northward was
Fred Halpert who settled into this relaxing bistro with
its gorgeous terrace overlooking the vineyards and a
nearby stream. Inside you'll find a charming rustic dining
area with an eclectic daily menu. Signature dishes are
portobello mushroom salad, osso bucco, and sea bass.
Though some warn of a recent downhill trend, all agree
the panoramic view is delightful. **Honors:** *Wine
Spectator*'s Award of Excellence (13 ratings/mixed)

68 60 61 83

Brennan's
American (Hofbrau) $

Reserv: Not accepted
Dress: Informal
Pay: M, V
Parking: Yes
Handicap Access: Yes
Bar: Full
Hours: Daily 11am-9:30pm

4th & University Ave
Berkeley   510-841-0960

This place has a history that dates back to an 1878
saloon and it shows. It's comfortable, from the hofbrau-
style cafeteria where you'll find seniors, college
students, professors, and tourists piling their trays with
huge slices of roast turkey and beef with all the trim-
mings right down to the renowned Irish coffees. Good
for groups, families, thrifty budgets, and lots of people
watching. (30 ratings/consistent)

81 75 69 79

Britt-Marie's
Continental $$

Reserv: Not accepted
Dress: Informal
Pay: Checks
Parking: No
Handicap Access: Yes
Bar: Beer/wine/separate
Hours: Tu-Sa 11:30am-2pm,
5:30-11pm; Su 5-10pm

1369 Solano Ave
Albany   510-527-1314

A neighborhood wine bar that captures the essence of a
cozy east European cafe where you can sip on a glass of
wine while reading a book, or settle down to a meal of
comforting favorites like goulash, roast chicken, or
schnitzel and noodles. A number of daily specials
always include fish and their ever-popular risotto. Good
for groups, singles, or intimate dates, the staff is casual
and friendly, and best of all, the prices are just right.
(32 ratings/consistent)

Food **Service** **Ambience** **Value**

74	71	54	76

Brothers Delicatessen
Deli
$

Reserv: Accepted
Dress: Informal
Pay: AE, DC, M, V
Parking: No
Handicap Access: Yes
Bar: Beer/wine
Hours: Daily 8am-8:30pm

1351 Howard Ave
Burlingame 650-343-2311

A haven for displaced New Yorkers longing for a real Kosher deli, come here when you're hungry—the servings of corned beef, pastrami, and potato pancakes are mammoth and warrant serious famine. Recently taken over by new owners, some complain that the quality has suffered, but the prices remain low and the values solid. Don't come here looking for atmosphere; it's strictly New York cafeteria—lots of bustle and noise. Outdoor dining. (38 ratings/mixed)

86	83	73	73

Buon Gusto
Italian
$$$

Reserv: Suggested
Dress: Informal
Pay: AE, M, V
Parking: No
Handicap Access: Yes
Bar: Beer/wine
Hours: M-F 11:30am-3pm,
5-10pm; Sa&Su 5-11pm

224 Grand Ave
S San Francisco 650-742-9777

Your Sicilian grandmother would love the authentic food and friendly service at this family-run trattoria that wins converts with each entering patron. All the comforting classics are prepared with a touch of the old-world—homemade gnocchi, lasagna, and cannelloni, combined with slow-cooked sauces, or veal that's rich and light. To avoid any pitfalls steer clear of desserts, then settle back and enjoy the timeless atmosphere. (15 ratings/mixed)

74	60	56	75

Cactus Taqueria
Mexican
$

Reserv: Not accepted
Dress: Informal
Pay: M, V
Parking: No
Area: Rockridge
Handicap Access: Yes
Bar: Beer/wine
Hours: Daily 11am-10pm
(Su 9pm)

5525 College Ave
Oakland 510-547-1305

The streetside atmosphere is festive at this local stop that features some unusual south-of-the-border specialties along with an eclectic collection of beers, all ordered cafeteria-style. Don't come here if you want standard fare, but do try their "burrito variety galore," chicken in mole, or homemade chicken tamales. Don't miss the salsas. At the end you'll still have enough money for an order of flan and a traditional caramel-filled cookie. Outdoor dining. (27 ratings/mixed)

74 71 69 76

Cafe de la Paz
Latin American $$

Reserv: Suggested
Dress: Informal
Pay: AE, M, V, Checks
Parking: Yes
Handicap Access: Yes
Bar: Beer/wine
Hours: M-F 11:45am-2:30pm,
5:30-9:30pm (F 10pm); Sa&Su
10am-2:30pm, 5-10pm (Su
9:30pm)

1600 Shattuck Ave
Berkeley   510-843-0662

A tantalizing selection of Central and South American foods is offered at this vibrant cafe that breathes new life into the local ethnic dining scene. The menu emphasizes chicken and vegetables in refreshingly new forms like empanadas, tapas, chimichurris, tamales, and some excellent Brazilian stews. Weekend brunch brings on corn pancakes, Caribbean hash, and chilaquiles. Service can be inexperienced, but reflects a dedication to the cause. (23 ratings/consistent)

---

77 77 75 80

Cafe Enrico
Italian $$$

Reserv: Suggested
Dress: Informal
Pay: AE, Disc, M, V
Parking: Yes
Area: Harbor Bay Isle
Handicap Access: Yes
Bar: Full/separate
Hours: Tu-F 11:30am-2:30pm,
4-10pm; Sa 4-10pm; Su 4-9pm

875-D Island Dr
Alameda   510-522-0128

Don't be fooled by its offbeat locale, this unpretentious favorite with its view of Harbor Bay lagoon has a staunch, dedicated following who never leave feeling they've been taken for a ride. Amply proportioned entrees come with lots of extras and satisfy even the heartiest diners. For the more thrifty, there are great early bird specials (Tu–F, 4–6pm). House specials include seafood capellini, broiled king salmon, and lamb chops with portobello mushrooms. (16 ratings/consistent)

81 71 68 63

Cafe Fanny
Breakfast/Lunch $

Reserv: Not accepted
Dress: Informal
Pay: M, V, Checks
Parking: Yes
Handicap Access: Ltd
Bar: Beer/wine
Hours: M-F 7am-3pm; Sa&Su
8am-3pm (Sa 4pm)

1603 San Pablo Ave
Berkeley   510-524-5447

This is fast food elevated to the ultimate level of California cuisine where everything is fresh and innovative. The limited menu features breakfast and lunch only, and though meals here are inexpensive, don't expect a lot for your money—this is food for the enlightened who've come for Alice Water's fare at affordable prices. The postage-stamp-sized space is often packed with foodies who spill out into the adjacent parking lot where there's seating. (15 ratings/consistent)

Food	Service	Ambience	Value

85 **79** **76** **74**

Cafe Kati
East-West $$$$

Reserv: Required
Dress: Informal
Pay: M, V
Parking: No
Area: Japantown
Handicap Access: Ltd
Bar: Beer/wine
Hours: Tu-Su 5:30-10pm

1963 Sutter St
San Francisco   415-775-7313

"Designed for the diner who wants an adventure"
(Miller), a meal at this noisy cafe will show you what
fusion cuisine is all about. The focus is on creativity,
both in the kitchen and on the plate; the end result is
"flamboyant inventiveness" (Miller) at a good price.
Though the menu changes monthly, you'll usually see
spring rolls, duck, salmon, and crème brûlée.
Professional service can help with wine selections.
Honors: Miller A-/B (23 ratings/mixed)

82 **77** **70** **78**

Cafe Riggio
Italian $$$

Reserv: Not accepted
Dress: Informal
Pay: M, V
Parking: No
Area: Richmond
Handicap Access: Yes
Bar: Full
Hours: M-Sa 5-10pm (F&Sa
11pm); Su 4:30-10pm

4112 Geary Blvd
San Francisco   415-221-2114

The inevitable sardine can pre-meal wait here doesn't
seem to deter anyone and, in fact, sets a convivial mood
for what's to come. Once seated, service is brisk and
wastes no time bringing such specialties as spinach
salad with squid, seafood cannelloni, roasted sea bass,
and a heavenly tiramisu; all reasonably priced. The
noise and bustle make this a good place for kids and
for groups. Reservations are taken for parties of six or
more. (19 ratings/consistent)

75 **69** **64** **75**

Caffe Delle Stelle
Italian $$

Reserv: Required
Dress: Informal
Pay: AE, DC, Disc, M, V
Parking: No
Area: Civic Center
Handicap Access: Yes
Bar: Wine
Hours: M-Sa noon-3pm,
5-10pm; Su 5-10pm

395 Hayes St
San Francisco   415-252-1110

A true slice of Italy near the Civic Center that serves
"simple and straightforward" (Bauer/Davis) pastas that
echo their rustic origins, grilled seafood, heavenly
tiramisu, and several country wines at very approach-
able prices. The "warm and homey" (Bauer/Davis)
atmosphere accented by a collection of wine and
vinegar bottles, is usually packed with a variety of
patrons, so reserve early seating if you're headed to a
show. (36 ratings/consistent)

Food	Service	Ambience	Value

81 **75** **66** **81**

The Cambodiana's
Cambodian $$

Reserv: Suggested
Dress: Informal
Pay: AE, DC, M, V
Parking: No
Handicap Access: Yes
Bar: Beer/wine
Hours: M-F 11:30am-3pm,
5-9:30pm (F 10:30pm); Sa 5-
10:30pm; Su 5-9:30pm

2156 University Ave
Berkeley 510-843-4630

An out-of-the-ordinary menu greets you at the pleasant cafe where first you opt for one of seven sauces offered, then decide what you want in it. Many items are decidedly French without the prices, such as grilled lamb or frog legs, but an eastern influence is also evident in smoked eggplant, catfish, salmon curry, or ginger blossom sauce. If you need help, the gracious staff will be glad to oblige. (35 ratings/consistent)

83 **85** **87** **69**

Campton Place
American $$$$$

Reserv: Suggested
Dress: Coat/tie suggested
Pay: AE, DC, M, V
Parking: No
Area: Union Square
Handicap Access: Yes
Bar: Full/separate
Hours: M-F 7am-10:30am,
11:30am-2pm, 6-10pm (F 5:30-
10:30pm); Sa 8am-2pm, 5:30-
10pm; Su 8am-2pm, 6-9:30pm

340 Stockton St
San Francisco 415-781-5555

East and west meet in this luxurious restaurant that delivers creative cutting-edge dishes in an atmosphere of quiet elegance. Look for tuna tartare, foie gras, lobster, and fixed-price offerings. Service is professional and well-paced. To defray high costs, raters recommend Wednesday Martini nights when there's a band and a bar menu, or Sunday brunch.
Honors: Bauer ★★★½, *Gourmet*, *Wine Spectator*'s Award of Excellence (30 ratings/mixed)

70 **75** **67** **76**

The Cape Cod
Continental $$$

Reserv: Accepted
Dress: Informal
Pay: AE, DC, Disc, M, V
Parking: No
Handicap Access: Yes
Bar: Beer/wine
Hours: Tu-F 11:30am-2pm,
5-10pm; Sa&Su 5-10pm

1150 Solano Ave
Albany 510-528-3308

The early bird specials can't be beat at this comfortable place that's heavily weighted in the seafood department, with a few pastas thrown in for good measure. Popular choices include the poached salmon with dill sauce and sole stuffed with crab, shrimp, and mushrooms. Some raters complain of small portions, especially when the food is so good. The atmosphere should put you at ease, as does the friendly and leisurely service. Outdoor dining. (13 ratings/mixed)

71 **65** **68** **77**

Capp's Corner
Italian   **$$**

Reserv: Accepted
Dress: Informal
Pay: AE, DC, Disc, M, V
Parking: No
Area: North Beach
Handicap Access: Ltd
Bar: Full
Hours: M-F 11:30am-2:30pm,
4:30-10:30pm; Sa&Su 4:30-
10:30pm

1600 Powell St
San Francisco   415-989-2589

A true San Francisco experience wouldn't be complete
without a visit to this audacious old-timer where you
wedge yourself into a chair at a red-and-white oilcloth
table and join in on the fun. Huge portions of family-
style favorites, like calamari, osso bucco, veal shanks,
and seafood cannelloni come with several courses at
low prices. That's why this place is famous. Don't
expect gourmet food, just gather a group and be ready
for a celebration. (22 ratings/consistent)

81 **77** **88** **76**

The Caprice
California   **$$$$**

Reserv: Suggested
Dress: Informal
Pay: AE, DC, M, V
Parking: Yes
Handicap Access: Yes
Bar: Full/separate
Hours: Daily 5-10pm

2000 Paradise Dr
Tiburon   415-435-3400

This '50's holdout teeters on the brink of the bay giving
diners some breathtaking views of Angel Island, the
Golden Gate, and the city beyond. The food, however,
is pure '90's: seared sea scallops, braised lamb shank,
shellfish paella, and duck breast with polenta. All
together you have an outstanding place to take out-of-
town visitors for an evening on the town or for Sunday
brunch. Outdoor dining. **Honors:** *Wine Spectator*'s
Award of Excellence (15 ratings/consistent)

81 **83** **91** **72**

Carnelian Room
American   **$$$$**

Reserv: Suggested
Dress: Coat/tie required
Pay: AE, DC, Disc, M, V
Parking: No
Area: Financial District
Handicap Access: Yes
Bar: Full/separate
Hours: Daily 6-9:30pm

555 California St, 52nd Floor
San Francisco   415-433-7500

You can't beat the soaring views from this penthouse
restaurant perched atop the Bank of America. Nor can
you avoid the high prices. Some recommend ordering
hors d'oeuvres with cocktails or wine, then going else-
where for dinner. If you do stay, expect good food and
polished service in a plush, romantic setting. Best bets
are the three-course prix-fixe dinners and Sunday
brunch. Good for groups. **Honors:** *Wine Spectator*'s
Grand Award (34 ratings/mixed)

| Food | Service | Ambience | Value |

78 **74** **70** **75**

Casa Orinda
American/Italian $$$

Reserv: Accepted
Dress: Informal
Pay: AE, M, V, Checks
Parking: Valet only (dinner)
Handicap Access: Yes
Bar: Full
Hours: Daily 4-10pm (F&Sa 11pm)

20 Bryant Way
Orinda 925-254-2981

"Big, comforting portions" (Saekel) in a wild Western roadhouse that was once a gambling joint, where the food harks "back to its Western lounge roots" (Himmel), yet only top-quality ingredients are used. As a result, fried chicken is antibiotic-free, the beef is organic, and the bread is from Acme. Best, though, is the universal appeal from the "heavenly" deep fried zucchini (Byrd), to the "terrific" mud pie (Himmel). **Honors:** Byrd A/A, Himmel★★★ (32 ratings/consistent)

69 **70** **64** **78**

CC Ole's
Mexican $$

Reserv: Suggested
Dress: Informal
Pay: AE, DC, Disc, M, V
Parking: Yes
Handicap Access: Yes
Bar: Full/separate
Hours: M-F 11am-10pm; Sa 10am-10pm; Su 11am-11pm

4633 Clayton Rd
Concord 925-798-1800

A madhouse on weekends, the locals pack in here for the fun, noisy, festive atmosphere complete with parrots and Mexican pottery that's perfect for family outings. Plan to abandon your diets. House favorites like the fajitas, enchilada Cancun, steaks, and chile colorado come in huge, satisfying portions that have staying power, as does the weekend brunch.
(25 ratings/consistent)

75 **72** **70** **76**

Celia's
Mexican $$

Reserv: Not accepted
Dress: Informal
Pay: AE, M, V
Parking: Yes
Handicap Access: Yes
Bar: Full/separate
Hours: M-Sa 11am-10:30pm (F&Sa 11pm); Su 11am-10pm

504 Peninsula Ave
San Mateo 650-343-5886

Fans of this small chain keep coming back for the enormous portions of south-of-the-border favorites served here. There are no surprises—the food's more Americanized than authentic, but the service is perky and the atmosphere is pleasant, though boisterous, and welcoming to large groups, kids, or singles who want a decent margarita. House specials include combo platters, fajitas, and cheese enchiladas. Live mariachi music on Wednesdays. (19 ratings/mixed)

87	**74**	**79**	**85**	Cha Cha Cha	$

Cha Cha Cha
Caribbean

Reserv: Not accepted
Dress: Informal
Pay: M, V
Parking: No
Area: Upper Haight
Handicap Access: Yes
Bar: Beer/wine
Hours: Daily 11:30am-4pm,
5-11pm (F&Sa 11:30pm)

1801 Haight St
San Francisco 415-386-5758

And the beat goes on at this noisy, vibrantly wild hangout where there's always a wait for a table. But the locals are in on its secret—order a pitcher of fruity sangria and get in the mood; you're in for some of the best tropical food around, at low prices. For tapas try the mussels, shrimp in coconut sauce, fried plantains, and pork quesadillas. For entrees, look for the roast pork leg or jerked chicken. Service is leisurely.
Honors: *Gourmet* (14 ratings/consistent)

80	**64**	**65**	**75**	Cha-Am	$

Cha-Am
Thai

Reserv: Accepted
Dress: Informal
Pay: AE, M, V
Parking: No
Handicap Access: Yes
Bar: Beer/wine
Hours: M-Sa 11:30am-3:30pm,
5-9:30pm (F&Sa 10pm); Su 5-
9:30pm

1543 Shattuck Ave
Berkeley 510-848-9664

There's a glass-covered patio dining area with sidewalk views at this popular neighborhood spot that's known for its spicy and fresh ingredients. The Dom-Ka Gai chicken soup is practically legendary, but don't overlook the roast duck, pad Thai, ginger shrimp, or curried salmon, when offered. Service can be slow at times, especially when it's busy, but the reasonable prices seem to make up for it. Good for groups and for family-style dining. (35 ratings/consistent)

79	**75**	**71**	**75**	Chef Chu's	$$

Chef Chu's
Chinese

Reserv: Suggested
Dress: Informal
Pay: AE, DC, M, V
Parking: Yes
Handicap Access: Yes
Bar: Full/separate
Hours: M-F 11:30am-9:30pm
(F 10pm); Sa&Su noon-10pm
(Su 9:30pm)

1067 N San Antonio Rd
Los Altos 650-948-2696

This peninsula institution may be criticized for its lack of authenticity, but the food is solid and the patrons are dedicated. Testament to the kitchen's skills are the ever-present throngs waiting at the door. Specialties of the house include hot and sour soup, moo sho pork, shredded chicken salad, whole-braised fish, curry chow fun, and won ton soup. If you don't have the appetite to try them all, get a copy of their cookbook for use at home. Outdoor dining. (72 ratings/mixed)

Food	Service	Ambience	Value

94 86 83 82 | Chef Paul's
French $$$

Reserv: Suggested
Dress: Informal
Pay: AE, Disc, M, V, Checks
Parking: No
Handicap Access: Yes
Bar: Beer/wine
Hours: Daily 5pm-midnight

4179 Piedmont Ave
Oakland 510-547-2175

This is the hands-down-winner for THE BEST FOOD in the Bay Area. Not only do raters call it "a real find" that's "still undiscovered," they award kudos to its top-notch service as well. Located on the second story, an expansive deck peeks over the street below, while inside, the dining area is quiet and intimate. The true winners are the very reasonable fixed-price menus packed with "elegant, rich" delicacies that reveal the "fantastic" chef's talent. (14 ratings/consistent)

76 75 68 75 | Chevy's
Mexican $$

Reserv: Accepted
Dress: Informal
Pay: AE, Disc, M, V
Parking: Yes
Handicap Access: Yes
Bar: Full/separate
Hours: Daily 11am-10pm
(F&Sa 11pm)

650 Ellinwood Way
Pleasant Hill 925-685-6651

Even after a decade, this blossoming chain is still packed with patrons waiting for hot chips and salsa, fajitas of every kind, and pitchers of margaritas. For many, the draw is the light and healthy fare that's made from scratch so that it's fresh on your plate. Splashy bright colors paint a carnival-like setting that's perfect for children, groups, and celebrations. Outdoor dining. See Quick-Check Table ratings for eight other area locations. **Honors:** *Focus* Best for Kids (33 ratings/consistent)

84 79 78 71 | Chez Panisse Cafe
California $$$

Reserv: Suggested
Dress: Informal
Pay: AE, DC, Disc, M, V, Checks
Parking: No
Handicap Access: Yes
Bar: Beer/wine
Hours: M-Sa 11:30am-3pm
(F&Sa 4pm), 5-10:30pm (F&Sa
11:30pm)

1517 Shattuck Ave
Berkeley 510-548-5049

This upstairs offshoot of the full service restaurant below offers first-rate cuisine on an a la carte basis and in a much more casual atmosphere. The daily menu features salads, pizzettas, and a few entrees. There's usually a line out the door even though some raters say it's overrated and has waitstaff with attitude, but patrons do get a glimpse of real California cuisine at prices that are within reason. (73 ratings/mixed)

Food **Service** **Ambience** **Value**

| 84 | 80 | 79 | 72 |

Chez Panisse Restaurant $$$$$
California

Reserv: Required
Dress: Coat/tie suggested
Pay: AE, DC, Disc, M, V. Checks
Parking: No
Handicap Access: Yes
Bar: Beer/wine
Hours: M-Sa 6-8pm, 8:30-10:30pm

1517 Shattuck Ave
Berkeley 510-548-5525

The food revolution of California cuisine began in this modest Victorian house almost three decades ago. Now an American legend, the focus here is still on the freshest and best ingredients available and the meals are all prix fixe. If you can get in, plan on either an incredible world class meal or the disappointment of small portions, high prices, and aloof service. **Honors:** Byrd A+/A+, *Focus* Best and Best East Bay, *Wine Spectator*'s Best of Award of Excellence (29 ratings/very mixed)

| 86 | 82 | 81 | 69 |

Chez TJ $$$$$
French

Reserv: Suggested
Dress: Informal
Pay: AE, M, V
Parking: No
Handicap Access: Yes
Bar: Beer/wine
Hours: Tu-Sa 5:30-9pm

938 Villa St
Mountain View 650-964-7466

Formal service, classical music, and daily fixed-price menus tell you that this is not a place for a fast bite before the movies, but rather a place to really savor a meal. Some complain that the high prices restrict it to special occasions only, while others say the elegant, refined food that's "artfully balanced" with fabulous presentations, and the classic desserts that "end a meal perfectly" (Davis) are definitely worth it. Outdoor dining. **Honors:** Davis★★½ (23 ratings/mixed)

| 81 | 86 | 82 | 80 |

China Chili $$
Chinese

Reserv: Suggested
Dress: Informal
Pay: AE, DC, M, V
Parking: Yes
Handicap Access: Yes
Bar: Full
Hours: M-Sa 11am-2pm, 5-9:30pm; Su 5-9:30pm

39116 State St
Fremont 510-791-1688

A melodic player piano greets you in the lobby of this atypical strip mall restaurant. The food, too, is unique— look for the honeyed pecan prawns, the garlic green beans, Mongolian beef, and daily specials. If you can't decide what to order, try the family dinners, or ask for suggestions from the helpful staff. Great for groups and family celebrations. (13 ratings/mixed)

Food **Service** **Ambience** **Value**

77	76	73	78

Christophe
California $$$$

Reserv: Suggested
Dress: Informal
Pay: AE, DC, M, V
Parking: No
Area: Union Square
Handicap Access: Yes
Bar: Full
Hours: W&Sa 11:30am-2pm;
Daily 5:30-9:30pm

320 Mason St
San Francisco   415-771-6393

This theatre district spot, purely Art-Deco with its peach walls, Erte prints, and potted palms, is adept at getting the throngs in and out before call time. There's always a pre-performance fixed menu in addition to regular offerings, that receive only mixed plaudits, and your servers know how to gauge the timing without blinking an eye. Favorite dishes include Caesar salad, chicken in peanut sauce, and lamb. (18 ratings/very mixed)

82	79	71	79

Christophe
French $$$

Reserv: Required
Dress: Informal
Pay: M, V
Parking: Yes
Handicap Access: No
Bar: Beer/wine
Hours: Tu-Su 5:30-10pm

1919 Bridgeway
Sausalito   415-332-9244

Regular patrons of this North Bay favorite say the best way to make its elegant fare affordable is to come in before 6pm when you can get a four-course prix-fixe menu for practically pennies. It's also the best time to try for a table if you're making plans at the last minute, since the place is small and usually packed. The salmon appetizer gets a special mention, as do the sweetbreads, cassoulet, lamb filet, and profiteroles and créme brûlée for dessert. (21 ratings/consistent)

84	78	70	75

Citron
Mediterranean $$$

Reserv: Suggested
Dress: Informal
Pay: AE, DC, Disc, M, V, Checks
Parking: No
Handicap Access: Ltd
Bar: Beer/wine
Hours: M-Th 5:30-9pm (W&Th 9:30pm); F&Sa 5:30-10pm; Su 5-9pm

5484 College Ave
Oakland   510-653-5484

A number of recent changes here have been subtle but the end result is better food with a slightly more focused execution; the meals remain top-notch. Though the menu changes every two weeks, look for seafood, "succulent" duck, "balanced and satisfying" lamb chops, or fabulous stuffed quail (Fowler). The stylish and homey interior is fresh and comfortable. Outdoor dining. **Honors:** Fowler★★★½
(62 ratings/consistent)

Food **Service** **Ambience** **Value**

| **77** | **76** | **75** | **79** |

City of Paris
Bistro
$$$

Reserv: Suggested
Dress: Informal
Pay: AE, DC, Disc, M, V
Parking: Valet only
Area: Union Square
Handicap Access: Yes
Bar: Full/separate
Hours: Daily 7am-9pm

101 Shannon Alley
San Francisco   415-441-4442

Tucked in a conveniently located alley, this casual spot attracts the pre-theatre crowd who come for the fixed-price menu and straightforward reasonably-priced bistro fare like spinach salad with duck confit, raclette, braised lamb shanks, and roast chicken. Though many say this is not a place for award-winning meals, it is still reliable, with decent service, and the location is prime for those who are off for entertainment elsewhere or want weekend brunch. (17 ratings/consistent)

| **71** | **68** | **69** | **75** |

Coleman Still
Cajun
$$

Reserv: Suggested
Dress: Informal
Pay: AE, DC, Disc, M, V
Parking: Yes
Handicap Access: Ltd
Bar: Full/separate
Hours: M-Sa 9am-10pm (F&Sa 11pm); Su 9am-9pm

1240 Coleman Ave
Santa Clara   408-727-4670

Despite all the hoopla over haute dining, our raters, though mixed in their opinions, still single out this place for its great kickback country meals. Housed in an old barnwood building that looks like it dates back to the '49ers, the decor of Mason jars and kerosene lanterns, and the food (hushpuppies, catfish, bread pudding, hearty breakfasts) will take you back a century. Old timers and kids seem equally comfortable here, and the prices aren't bad. (26 ratings/mixed)

| **73** | **78** | **57** | **84** |

Country Way
American
$$

Reserv: Not accepted
Dress: Informal
Pay: M, V
Parking: Yes
Handicap Access: Yes
Bar: Beer/wine
Hours: Daily 6am-10:30pm (Su 10pm)

5325 Mowry Ave
Fremont   510-797-3188

Comfortable family dining at its best in a minimal setting; portions are huge, prices are low, and the three-page menu guarantees something for everyone. Like the truck-stop coffee shops of yore, breakfasts of hot cakes, pork chops, and omelets are served anytime. Lunch and dinner selections range from sandwiches, salads and burgers, to steak, roast beef, liver, pastas, and seafood plates. Amazingly, prices for either lunch or dinner remain the same. (21 ratings/consistent)

| Food | Service | Ambience | Value |

88 **85** **83** **67**

Dal Baffo
Continental $$$$$

Reserv: Suggested
Dress: Coat/tie suggested
Pay: AE, DC, M, V
Parking: Yes
Handicap Access: Yes
Bar: Full
Hours: M-F 11:30am-2pm, 5-10pm; Sa 5-10pm

878 Santa Cruz Ave
Menlo Park 650-325-1588

The place for a special celebration, especially when you want to don your dress-up clothes and challenge your credit limit. In return you get superb European fare served in grand elegance on crystal and china. Best bets on the menu are the fillet of beef, the rack of veal, and the daily pastas. The hefty wine list (more like a wine volume) is considered to be one of the best in the country. (40 ratings/consistent)

72 **71** **72** **75**

Delancy Street
American $$

Reserv: Suggested
Dress: Informal
Pay: AE, M, V, Checks
Parking: Valet only
Area: South of Market
Handicap Access: Yes
Bar: Beer/wine/separate
Hours: Tu-F 11am-3pm, 5:30-10:30pm; Sa&Su 10am-3pm, 5:30-10:30pm

600 Embarcadero St
San Francisco 415-512-5179

The organization behind this waterfront restaurant works for good social causes, so it's easy to forgive an occasional lapse. The menu is global, so on any given day, you'll probably find something from diverse regions of the world. Stick to the simplest fare or come for high tea in the afternoon. The interior is pure bistro, with lots of pastels and a copper bar, and there's a glassed-in patio area for great bay views. Weekend brunch. (47 ratings/consistent)

71 **69** **60** **81**

Des Alpes
Basque $$

Reserv: Required weekends
Dress: Informal
Pay: M, V
Parking: No
Area: North Beach
Handicap Access: Yes
Bar: Full/separate
Hours: Tu-Th 5-9:30pm; F&Sa 5:30-10pm; Su 5-9:30pm

732 Broadway
San Francisco 415-391-4249

Robust, family-style dining sets the theme at this charming spot that's been serving traditional meals from the Pyrenees for almost a century. Each day offers a new staggering seven-course fixed-price menu, as well as regular dinner fare. Specialties include lamb and oxtail stews, sweetbreads, trout, and soup. The air is boisterous as the jocular staff just keeps bringing in more platters for patrons to pass. Great for groups and for good dining deals. (14 ratings/consistent)

Food	Service	Ambience	Value

73 **72** **67** **76**

Di Cicco's
Italian   **$$$**

Reserv: Suggested
Dress: Informal
Pay: AE, DC, Disc, M, V
Parking: Yes
Handicap Access: Ltd
Bar: Beer/wine
Hours: M-F 11am-11pm (F midnight); Sa&Su 11am-10pm (Sa midnight)

2509 S Bascom Ave
Campbell   408-377-5850

In an era when Italian fare seems to be expensive chic or cheap mediocre, this popular place falls somewhere in between. Despite some complaints of a tired menu, there are many good choices for the price, so if you select carefully, you can dine very well. Good bets are the traditional pastas, veal, chicken, and seafood. The atmosphere is comfortable with cheerful service, and live guitar music on Wednesdays and Saturdays. (18 ratings/mixed)

---

84 **79** **70** **78**

The Diner
California/Mexican   **$$**

Reserv: Suggested
Dress: Informal
Pay: Checks
Parking: Yes
Handicap Access: Yes
Bar: Beer/wine
Hours: Tu-Su 8am-3pm, 5:30-9pm (F&Sa 10pm)

6476 Washington St
Yountville   707-944-2626

The name can be misleading. This hot spot with mixed ratings is usually packed with locals and tourists who come for the comforting classic breakfasts of latkes, omelets, cornmeal pancakes, and french toast served in a casual setting. Lunch and dinner menus take a south-of-the-border turn with burritos, rellenos, and combination plates, plus a number of burgers, sandwiches, salads, and homemade favorites like chicken piccata, meat loaf, and fresh fish. (14 ratings/mixed)

---

91 **88** **89** **75**

Domaine Chandon
French   **$$$$$**

Reserv: Required
Dress: Coat/tie suggested
Pay: AE, DC, Disc, M, V
Parking: Yes
Handicap Access: Yes
Bar: Wine/separate
Hours: Daily 11:30am-2:30pm; W-Su 6-9:30pm (closed M&Tu Nov-Apr)

1 California Dr
Yountville   707-944-2892

This landmark wine country destination that raters herald for exemplary food, the beautiful terrace setting among the vines, fixed-price dinners, and excellent service has seen some recent changes. The menu has been "simplified into a more straightforward brasserie style" (Bauer) and the interior has been refreshed. High scores for food, service and ambience match the final bill. **Honors:** Bauer★★, *Wine Spectator*'s Award of Excellence (45 ratings/consistent)

Food	Service	Ambience	Value

81	73	53	81

Doug's Bar-B-Q
BBQ $

Reserv: Not accepted
Dress: Informal
Pay: M, V
Parking: Yes
Handicap Access: No
Bar: None
Hours: M-Sa 11am-9pm (F&Sa midnight); Su noon-9pm

3600 San Pablo Ave
Emeryville 510-655-9048

Don't come here for the atmosphere; there isn't any except for the smoke-enriched take-out window that peers out over the local card rooms, beer joints, and street scene. Do come here for some of the best ribs, lamb, cajun chicken, and goat in the territory that you mop up with a wedge of soft white bread. Or try the deep-fried turkey or sweet potato pie that are stick-to-the-ribs real country. By the way, don't dress up—this is messy food at its best. (16 ratings/consistent)

84	79	83	80

Eight Forty North First
American $$$$

Reserv: Suggested
Dress: Informal
Pay: AE, DC, Disc, M, V
Parking: Yes
Handicap Access: Yes
Bar: Full/separate
Hours: M-F 11:30am-10pm; Sa 5-10pm

840 N 1st St
San Jose 408-282-0840

If watching masses of lawyers or city officials during the day is your thing, this is the place to go—at lunch there's a group exodus from City Hall just across the street. Fortunately at night the crowd thins out and tables are easier to get. The draw is the contemporary atmosphere and a highly praised east-west fusion menu, plus a fixed-price menu of game, fresh fish, veal, and rack of lamb. Service is attentive. The granite bar features brandies and single malts. (20 ratings/consistent)

82	83	90	74

El Paseo
French $$$$

Reserv: Suggested
Dress: Informal
Pay: AE, DC, Disc, M, V, Checks
Parking: No
Handicap Access: Yes
Bar: Beer/wine/separate
Hours: Tu-Su 5:30-10pm

17 Throckmorton Ave
Mill Valley 415-388-0741

"A meandering path" (Cianci) leads you through a flowering garden into intimate rooms that just drip with charm. There you'll find one of the most romantic settings in the Bay Area, perfect, raters say, for an anniversary. The menu of "classically inspired French fare" (Cianci) features duck liver mousse, steamed salmon, sliced duck breast, and tarte Tatin. Service is professional and attentive. Outdoor dining. **Honors:** Cianci★★, *Wine Spectator*'s Grand Award (21 ratings/consistent)

Food	Service	Ambience	Value		

72 73 75 75 — El Torito — $$
Mexican

Reserv: Accepted
Dress: Informal
Pay: AE, DC, Disc, M, V
Parking: Yes
Handicap Access: Yes
Bar: Full/separate
Hours: M-Sa 11am-11pm
(F&Sa midnight): Su 9:30am-
10pm

1961 Diamond Blvd
Concord 925-798-7660

"Surrender to the beat of the blender" is the motto of
this national chain where margaritas and tropical drinks
pave the way for mammoth portions of gringo-style food.
Favorites include fajitas, tacos, carne asada, and for the
really hungry, the macho combos. Answering complaints,
there are now many new low fat offerings. Reasonable
prices and a festive atmosphere make this a great place
for groups and Sunday brunch. See Quick-Check Table
ratings for Daly City location. (27 ratings/mixed)

84 79 73 88 — Eliza's — $
Chinese

Reserv: Suggested
Dress: Informal
Pay: M, V
Parking: No
Area: Civic Center
Handicap Access: Yes
Bar: Beer/wine
Hours: M-F 11am-3pm,
5-9pm; Sa 11am-9pm

205 Oak St
San Francisco 415-621-4819

Matisse-like murals, lights that resemble sea creatures,
Wedgewood cups, and colorful Italian plates set the
stage for the creative cuisine offered at this Civic Center
favorite. Raters say the outstanding food and low prices
make it one of the best bargains around. Don't miss the
spicy eggplant, sunflower beef, portobello mushrooms,
or symphony prawns. See Quick-Check Table for highly-
rated Potrero Hill location. (19 ratings/very consistent)

75 70 66 76 — Emil Villa's California BBQ — $$
BBQ

Reserv: Not accepted
Dress: Informal
Pay: AE, Disc, M, V
Parking: Yes
Area: Rockridge
Handicap Access: Yes
Bar: Beer/wine
Hours: Daily 6am-9pm

1982 Pleasant Valley Ave
Oakland 510-654-0915

The smiling pigs scampering all over the menu should
give you a clue—the "Pit" is pig-out heaven. Not much
has changed here in 60 years: coffee is poured as soon
as you settle into an upholstered booth; the slabs of
meat and ribs are still pit-smoked over hickory. Breakfasts too are still hearty and prices a throwback. See
Quick-Check Table ratings for Concord, Corte Madera,
Fremont, and Hayward locations.
(26 ratings/consistent)

90	86	80	75

Emile's
French $$$$$

Reserv: Suggested
Dress: Informal
Pay: AE, DC, Disc, M, V
Parking: Valet only
Handicap Access: Yes
Bar: Full
Hours: F 11:30am-2pm;
Tu-Sa 6-10pm

545 S 2nd St
San Jose   408-289-1960

This crown jewel of South Bay's exclusive restaurants
has had a few shakeups lately, but has weathered the
storm. Traditional dishes like a "standout" foie gras,
"perfect" pork tenderloin (Himmel), their signature
Grand Marnier soufflé, and the fixed-price menu are still
sublime, but not cheap. Fortunately, there's an excellent
wine list and attentive service to carry you through the
process. **Honors:** Himmel★★★½, *Wine Spectator*'s
Award of Excellence (22 ratings/consistent)

76	68	65	77

Esperpento
Spanish $

Reserv: Required
Dress: Informal
Pay: Cash Only
Parking: No
Area: Valencia
Handicap Access: Ltd
Bar: Full
Hours: M-F 11am-3pm,
5-10pm; Sa 11am-10:30pm

3295 22nd St
San Francisco   415-282-8867

Popular with the artsy crowd, this wacky spot, with its
strolling mariachis and vivid pink walls, sports a large
tapas menu where squid, paella, shrimp, chicken
croquettes, and garlic reign. A fixed price menu is
offered daily. Patrons are boisterous, especially on
weekends when the place is packed, so expect a wait.
If need be, a pitcher of sangria can dull the senses.
Outdoor dining. (15 ratings/mixed)

82	77	75	70

Eulipia
American $$$

Reserv: Suggested
Dress: Informal
Pay: AE, DC, Disc, M, V
Parking: No
Handicap Access: Yes
Bar: Full
Hours: Tu-F 11:30am-2pm,
5:30-10pm; Sa 5:30-10pm;
Su 4:30-9pm

374 South First St
San Jose   408-280-6161

For years the locals have been flocking here for the
health-conscious food, but recent changes have put it
on the cutting edge. The interior is sleekly comfortable
with al fresco dining, and the menu has expanded to
include new choices, while keeping them sizeable and
healthy. Look for the baked stuffed artichoke appetizer,
Idaho river trout, grilled chicken, lemon and lime pie,
or chocolate rum delice. Saavy service oversees all
details. (29 ratings/consistent)

| Food | Service | Ambience | Value |

82 **77** **77** **73**

Evvia
Greek $$$$

Reserv: Suggested
Dress: Informal
Pay: DC, M, V
Parking: Yes
Handicap Access: Yes
Bar: Full
Hours: M-F 11:30am-2:30pm.
5-10pm (F&Sa 11pm): Sa&Su 5-
11pm (Su 9pm)

420 Emerson St
Palo Alto   650-326-0983

The spirit of the Aegean has been revitalized and given a
California touch at this beautiful, sleek charmer that
boasts warm, friendly service. Once you enter, you're
enveloped in saffron-colored walls punctuated by a
huge rustic fireplace, and a brick spit churning the
specialties of the day. Excellent choices include pastas,
lamb, grilled meats, chicken, and fish, though the
classic moussaka and spinach fillo are wonderfully light
and tasty. (16 ratings/consistent)

77 **77** **71** **78**

Fabrizio's
Italian $$

Reserv: Suggested
Dress: Informal
Pay: AE, M, V
Parking: Yes
Handicap Access: Yes
Bar: Beer/wine
Hours: M-Sa 11:30am-10pm:
Su 4-10pm

455 Magnolia Ave
Larkspur   415-924-3332

Don't be put off by the minimal interior, all eyes here
focus on the kitchen whose sole purpose is to produce
excellent classic fare with a light touch for a reasonable
price. Many daily specials augment the regular menu
with favorites like Caesar salad, salmon piccata, grilled
chicken, filet of halibut, and a daily risotto that usually
rivals any you'll find in a first-class restaurant in the
city. Service is casual and warm, yet professional.
Outdoor dining. (21 ratings/consistent)

75 **72** **65** **77**

Fatapple's
American $$

Reserv: Not accepted
Dress: Informal
Pay: M, V
Parking: No
Handicap Access: Yes
Bar: Beer/wine
Hours: Daily 7am-10pm (F&Sa
11pm)

1346 M L King Jr Way
Berkeley   510-526-2260

There's usually a line at this no-frills restaurant that
churns out all the basics. Handmade chuck burgers
star, along with baked specialties that accompany the
ranch-style breakfasts, or pies that can't be beat. Lunch
and dinner menus include soups, fresh salads,
sandwiches, pot pies, spaghetti, and macaroni and
cheese, with shakes and malts on the side. Great family
dining at bargain prices. See Quick-Check Table for
highly-rated El Cerrito location. (38 ratings/consistent)

Food	Service	Ambience	Value

Firefly
California
$$$

81 **79** **68** **74**

Reserv: Suggested
Dress: Informal
Pay: AE, M, V, Checks
Parking: No
Area: Noe Valley
Handicap Access: Yes
Bar: Beer/wine
Hours: Daily 5:30-10:30pm

4288 24th St
San Francisco   415-821-7652

A "charming, warm neighborhood restaurant" whose "quirky menu" (Bauer) breaks the confines of the usual. You'll find Thai salmon cakes, seafood pot stickers, and roasted beet salad served alongside bayou gumbo, cassoulet with tofu and wild mushrooms, roast chicken with mole sauce, and all sorts of decadent desserts. Oddly enough, it all works. The bare-bones interior is always being revamped, and service is genuinely friendly.
Honors: Bauer★★½ (20 ratings/consistent)

Flea St Cafe
American
$$$$

81 **80** **83** **72**

Reserv: Suggested
Dress: Informal
Pay: AE, DC, M, V, Checks
Parking: Yes
Handicap Access: Yes
Bar: Beer/wine
Hours: Tu-F 11:30am-2pm,
5:30-9:30pm; Sa 5:30-9:30pm;
Su 10am-2pm, 5:30-9:30pm

3607 Alameda de las Pulgas
Menlo Park   650-854-1226

Take a small cottage farmhouse decorated with floral wallpaper and lace curtains, team it up with an organic menu that favors vegetables, and you have this endearing restaurant that raters call "wonderful" and "unusual." Try the salmon, green onion noodle cakes, and mushroom ravioli but be prepared: organic produce and meats can be expensive. Excellent service keeps it a smooth operation. Sunday brunch and outdoor dining. (40 ratings/consistent)

Fleur de Lys
French
$$$$$

90 **82** **90** **73**

Reserv: Accepted
Dress: Coat/tie suggested
Pay: AE, DC, M, V
Parking: Valet only
Area: Union Square
Handicap Access: Yes
Bar: Full
Hours: M-Th 6-9pm;
F&Sa 5:30-10:30pm

777 Sutter St
San Francisco   415-673-7779

This is one of the city's most visually stunning and opulent restaurants with a price tag to prove it. The romantic setting is unsurpassed and both a la carte and fixed-price menus feature cuisine that is heralded for its uncompromising quality and refinement—like foie gras, asparagus soup with caviar, salmon, and filet mignon. Desserts too, are elegant and superb.
Honors: *Focus* Best For A Date, *Wine Spectator*'s Best of Award of Excellence (41 ratings/consistent)

| **83** | **74** | **78** | **79** |

The Flying Saucer
California   **$$$$**

Reserv: Suggested
Dress: Coat/tie suggested
Pay: AE, M, V
Parking: No
Area: Mission
Handicap Access: Yes
Bar: Beer/wine
Hours: Tu-Sa 5:30-9:30pm
(F&Sa 10pm)

1000 Guerrero St
San Francisco   415-641-9955

The zany setting, which includes a huge bust of David
and a carnival ride car, looks like something out of a
Jetson's movie set. The complexities of the food can be
cosmic and somehow it all comes together in this
convivial, hip bistro. The worldly menu contains cross-
cultural samplings, masterfully presented. Specialties
include seared foie gras, roasted lobster, potato crust
bass, and desserts that are out of this world. Outdoor
dining. (17 ratings/consistent)

| **93** | **88** | **82** | **77** |

French Laundry
French   **$$$$$**

Reserv: Required
Dress: Informal
Pay: AE, M, V, Checks
Parking: No
Handicap Access: Yes
Bar: Beer/wine
Hours: M-Th 5:30-9:30pm;
F&Sa 11:30am-1:45pm, 5:30-
9:30pm; Su 11:30am-1:45pm

6640 Washington St
Yountville   707-944-2380

Gourmets flock here for leisurely paced "culinary
fantasias—prix fixe menus composed of many minia-
ture courses" (Unterman) that have earned chef/owner
Thomas Keller the nation's James Beard award and cost
a bundle. The setting, a century-old stone house with
lush gardens, could just as easily be in the French
countryside as in California. Excellent staff. Outdoor
dining. **Honors:** *Focus* Best North Bay,
Himmel★★★★ (16 ratings/consistent)

| **81** | **86** | **90** | **77** |

French Room
French   **$$$$$**

Reserv: Suggested
Dress: Coat/tie suggested
Pay: AE, DC, Disc, M, V
Parking: Valet only
Area: Theater District
Handicap Access: Yes
Bar: Full/separate
Hours: Daily 6:30am-2pm
(Sa&Su 7am), 5:30-10pm

495 Geary St
San Francisco   415-775-4700

The palatial setting marked by crystal chandeliers and
Louis XV furnishings steals the show here. Service, too,
treats patrons like royalty by pampering them with sil-
ver-domed plates filled with luxurious offerings like
lamb in filo, foie gras, lobster risotto, and roast duck.
Daily fixed-price and a la carte menus are available.
Sunday brunch and piano (W-Su). Outdoor dining.
Honors: *Wine Spectator*'s Grand Award
(13 ratings/mixed)

| 78 | 72 | 70 | 83 |

Fresh Choice $
American

Reserv: Not accepted
Dress: Informal
Pay: AE, M, V
Parking: Yes
Handicap Access: Yes
Bar: Beer/wine
Hours: M-Sa 11am-9pm;
Su 10am-9pm

555 E Calaveras Blvd
Milpitas   408-262-6604

This popular chain can't be beat for great, affordable, fast meals where self-service buffets are the bill of fare. Food bars include soups, salads, pastas, and baked items—plus many low-fat selections. The atmosphere is spartan but clean; most come here for thrifty, brisk meals and don't give a hoot about ambience. Great for families. Sunday brunch. See Quick-Check Table for seven other highly-rated locations in Bay Area.
Honors: *Focus* Best for Kids (23 ratings/mixed)

| 85 | 78 | 73 | 78 |

Fringale $$
Bistro

Reserv: Required
Dress: Informal
Pay: AE, M, V
Parking: No
Area: South of Market
Handicap Access: Yes
Bar: Full
Hours: M-F 11:30am-3pm;
M-Sa 5:30-10:30pm

570 4th St
San Francisco   415-543-0573

Although the competition has been stiff, this warm, cozy bistro "remains one of the best casual French restaurants in the city...and it's still a great deal" (Bauer). Raters complain of waits and cramped quarters, but say the award-winning rustic fare like cassoulet, rack of lamb, frisee salad, and the pork tenderloin confit makes up for it all.
Honors: Bauer★★★½ (78 ratings/consistent)

| 80 | 75 | 79 | 69 |

Fuki Sushi $$$$
Japanese

Reserv: Required
Dress: Informal
Pay: AE, DC, Disc, M, V
Parking: Yes
Handicap Access: Yes
Bar: Full
Hours: M-F 11:30am-2pm;
Daily 5-10pm (Su 9:30pm)

4119 El Camino Real
Palo Alto   650-494-9383

Leave your shoes at the door and settle into an attractive tatami room where kimono-clad waitstaff serves up a huge assortment of fresh sushi, light plates, and full multi-course meals including their signature shabu shabu—a do-it-yourself firepot that's always fun, especially for groups. Other signature dishes include the combination plates, tempura, and noodles. A menu of sushi platters for large groups is also available for takeout. Outdoor dining. (19 ratings/consistent)

88 **78** **74** **75** **Garden City** $$$$
Continental

Reserv: Suggested
Dress: Informal
Pay: AE, DC, M, V
Parking: Yes
Handicap Access: Ltd
Bar: Full/separate
Hours: M-F 11:30am-10pm;
Sa&Su 5-11 pm

360 South Saratoga Ave
San Jose 408-244-4443

There's a lot happening at this legendary supper club
that serves up your basic meat and potatoes fare with
huge slabs of prime rib, thick steaks, and grilled fish in
a dimly lit nightclub setting. To go along with your
meal, live jazz is featured nightly in the lounge, and
when you're finished with listening and eating, you can
head next door to the card room for some real late-
night action. **Honors:** *Wine Spectator's* Award of
Excellence (23 ratings/consistent)

---

84 **75** **85** **69** **The Garden Grill** $$$$
British

Reserv: Suggested
Dress: Informal
Pay: AE, DC, M, V, Checks
Parking: Yes
Handicap Access: Yes
Bar: Full/separate
Hours: M-Sa 3-5pm, 5:30-
10pm; Su 5:30-9pm

1026 Alma St
Menlo Park 650-325-8981

Dine in the English countryside at this sedate roadhouse
with tapestries and Asian carpets, or take full high tea
on the courtyard under the towering oak. Specialties
include Stilton cheese balls with port sauce, venison
with Cumberland sauce, and prawns in Irish whiskey.
The pub menu features Cornish pasties, Ploughman's
platters, and many more that you wash down with your
favorite ale. High tea is served daily except Sunday.
Outdoor dining. (13 ratings/consistent)

---

81 **78** **67** **77** **Garibaldi Cafe** $$$
California

Reserv: Suggested
Dress: Informal
Pay: AE, DC, M, V
Parking: Yes
Area: Potrero Hill
Handicap Access: Ltd
Bar: Full/separate
Hours: M-Sa 11:30am-2:30pm,
5:30-10pm

1600 17th St
San Francisco 415-552-3325

There's always a party at this chic sports bar with an
eclectic group of regulars who come for the thrifty
prices, generous portions, friendly service, and the draft
beer. Though the menu changes daily, you'll usually
find tandoori lamb, warm spinach salad, blackened
salmon, pastas, quesadillas, and burgers. For those who
think the corrugated aluminum interior is too strange,
there's outdoor dining and a special take-out window.
Live jazz on Saturday. (27 ratings/consistent)

80 | 79 | 76 | 77

Garibaldi's
California/Mediterranean $$$$

Reserv: Required
Dress: Informal
Pay: AE, M, V, Checks
Parking: Valet only
Area: Pacific Heights
Handicap Access: Ltd
Bar: Full
Hours: M-F 11:30am-2:30pm;
Daily 5:30-10pm (F&Sa
10:30pm)

347 Presidio Ave
San Francisco   415-563-8841

A popular neighborhood spot that keeps getting better,
partly because it serves some of the best lamb in town,
along with excellent fish and pasta dishes. The recently
remodeled setting is filled with pleasant artwork and
gorgeous floral displays to set the scene for a romantic
date. Though some call this a sleeper, its escalating
popularity sometimes brings crowds and noise, but the
accommodating and friendly staff always seems to take
it in stride. Sunday brunch. (17 ratings/very consistent)

81 | 75 | 72 | 71

Gaylord India
Indian $$$

Reserv: Suggested
Dress: Informal
Pay: AE, DC, Disc, M, V
Parking: Yes
Handicap Access: Yes
Bar: Full/separate
Hours: Daily 11:30am-2:30pm,
5-10pm

1706 El Camino Real
Menlo Park   650-326-8761

A recent move has taken this upscale serene restaurant
to a nearby location with larger quarters and a fresh
new look. The menu still features the Bombay chicken
wings tandoori, rich cashew-based chicken pasanda,
piquant tandoori swordfish, and several fragrant lamb
curries to pair with their house-baked breads. An
affordable lunch buffet is offered weekdays, and on
Sunday, a buffet brunch spans the entire menu. Formal
but accommodating service. (21 ratings/consistent)

79 | 76 | 67 | 80

Gira Polli
Italian $$

Reserv: Suggested
Dress: Informal
Pay: AE, M, V, Checks
Parking: No
Area: North Beach
Handicap Access: Ltd
Bar: Beer/wine
Hours: Daily 4:30-9:30pm

659 Union St
San Francisco   415-434-4102

This postage-stamp-sized place is where the secret of
superb roasted chicken all began. All three Bay Area
locations are dominated by huge wood-burning
rotisseries chock full of rotating birds waiting to be
eaten on the spot or scarfed up by enthusiastic take-out
customers. Antipastas, salads, pasta, and a not-to-be-
missed lemon cheesecake round out the menu. See
Quick-Check Table ratings for Mill Valley location.
Honors: *Focus* Best Takeout (14 ratings/consistent)

Food	Service	Ambience	Value

81 **75** **77** **77**

Golden Turtle
Vietnamese

$$$

Reserv: Suggested
Dress: Informal
Pay: AE, Disc, M, V
Parking: No
Area: Pacific Heights
Handicap Access: Yes
Bar: Beer/wine
Hours: Tu-Su 5-11pm

2211 Van Ness Ave
San Francisco   415-441-4419

The handcrafted delicacies that come out of this soothing, attractive restaurant are among the most intriguing in the city. Run by a husband and wife team, the emphasis in the kitchen is on clean and fresh flavors, a theme that sparks the grilled beef with lemongrass, or the tamarind crab that is ocean fresh, the vibrant five-spice chicken, or the crisp imperial rolls. The price for this dip into exotica is not much, and service is warm, but leisurely. (14 ratings/consistent)

77 **71** **71** **76**

Good Earth
California

$$

Reserv: Suggested
Dress: Informal
Pay: AE, DC, Disc, M, V
Parking: Yes
Handicap Access: Yes
Bar: Beer/wine
Hours: M-F 7:30am-9pm (F 10pm); Sa&Su 8am-10pm (Su 9pm)

2231 Larkspur Landing Circle
Larkspur   415-461-7322

A carry-over from 1980 that's still in step with current health-conscious dining. Fruit smoothies, yogurt shakes, and light breakfasts make way for salads, soups, and sandwiches for lunch. Popular dinner selections include broiled teriyaki chicken, islander chow mein, and tofu spinach ravioli. Patio dining. Weekend brunches. See Quick-Check Table ratings for five other area locations. (28 ratings/consistent)

75 **68** **60** **86**

Gourmet Carousel
Chinese

$

Reserv: Accepted
Dress: Informal
Pay: M, V
Parking: No
Area: Pacific Heights
Handicap Access: Yes
Bar: Beer/wine
Hours: Tu-Sa 11am-9:30pm; Su 4-9:30pm

1559 Franklin
San Francisco   415-771-2044

Group dining doesn't get any better, or cheaper, than at this out-of-the-way restaurant that's full of surprises. There's an entire menu page for family-style dining, plus tables equipped with Lazy Susans just for that purpose. The huge portions of high-quality specialties like pot stickers, walnut prawns, Peking duck, ginger crab, and curry noodles will convert you to a regular. Though the atmosphere is basic, service is very friendly. (13 ratings/consistent)

Food	Service	Ambience	Value

84 | 72 | 72 | 80 — Guernica — *Basque* — $$$

Reserv: Suggested
Dress: Informal
Pay: AE, DC, M, V
Parking: Yes
Handicap Access: Ltd
Bar: Full/separate
Hours: Daily 5-10pm

2009 Bridgeway
Sausalito 415-332-1512

Lamb shanks, sweetbreads, outstanding seafood, and paella Valenciana that's "the best" have kept this old-timer going for well over two decades. Other winners include the onion soup, pâté, and grilled chicken. Raters also commend the intimate, old-world setting with an antique oak sideboard that sets the scene for romance, especially after you've had the ambrosial créme caramel. Friendly owners and staff treat their regular patrons like family. (13 ratings/very consistent)

80 | 78 | 81 | 69 — Harris' — *Steak* — $$$$$

Reserv: Suggested
Dress: Coat/tie suggested
Pay: AE, DC, Disc, M, V
Parking: Valet only
Area: Pacific Heights
Handicap Access: Yes
Bar: Full/separate
Hours: M-F 6-10pm (F 10:30pm); Sa 5-10:30pm; Su 5-9:30pm

2100 Van Ness Ave
San Francisco 415-673-1888

The score's divided on this old-time steak, potatoes, and salad place with its clubby atmosphere of dark paneling and leatherette booths. The argument erupts over whether the high cost is worth every penny or simply outrageous. To decide for yourself, go for the martinis, Caesar salad, the aged New York steaks, while you enjoy professional service. Live jazz played Wednesday through Saturday. (44 ratings/mixed)

82 | 82 | 83 | 69 — Hawthorne Lane — *California* — $$$$$

Reserv: Suggested
Dress: Coat/tie suggested
Pay: DC, Disc, M, V, Checks
Parking: Valet only
Area: South of Market
Handicap Access: Yes
Bar: Full
Hours: M-F 11:30am-1:45pm; Daily 5:30-10pm (F&Sa 10:30pm)

22 Hawthorne St
San Francisco 415-777-9779

The theme at this unpretentious trendsetter is the interplay between big and small as evidenced by the exorbitant prices, miniscule portions, and larger-than-life spaces that can be noisy and intimidating. Nevertheless, raters say that dining here can be a terrific experience if you order foie gras, Sonoma lamb, steamed sea bass, or any of their stellar desserts. You'll enjoy the live piano music played nightly. **Honors:** *Focus* Best San Francisco Area (39 ratings/consistent)

Food	Service	Ambience	Value

87 **77** **80** **85** | ## Helmand
Afghan $$$

Reserv: Required weekends
Dress: Informal
Pay: AE, M, V
Parking: Yes
Area: North Beach
Handicap Access: Yes
Bar: Full
Hours: Daily 5:30-10pm (F&Sa 11pm)

430 Broadway
San Francisco   415-362-0641

An evening of intrigue awaits you at this unpretentious oasis whose food is unsurpassed. Though raters grouse about the lack of parking in the area, once in the door you'll relish unusual specialties like their signature aushak-leek ravioli, baked pumpkin kaddo, seekh kababs, and sheerekh parfait. Service is refined, as is the serene setting graced with subdued lighting, fresh flowers, and Middle Eastern artifacts.
(35 ratings/consistent)

80 **72** **67** **80** | ## Henry's World Famous Hi-Life
BBQ $$$

Reserv: Accepted
Dress: Informal
Pay: AE, M, V
Parking: Yes
Handicap Access: Ltd
Bar: Full/separate
Hours: M 5-9pm; Tu-Th 11:30am-2pm, 5-9pm; F 11:30am-2pm, 4-10pm; Sa 4-10pm; Su 5-9pm

301 W St John St
San Jose   408-295-5414

The roadhouse setting belies the name, but one look at this place and you know it's been serving steaks, ribs, chicken, and mushrooms for the hungry and thrifty for a long, long time. Years of smoke from the barbecue have weathered the place, peeled the paint, and made it generally dingy, but the fare hasn't changed. Some raters say that it's depressing and the food's only fair; others just love the place, warts and all.
(19 ratings/very mixed)

80 **71** **69** **81** | ## Hobee's
American $

Reserv: Not accepted
Dress: Informal
Pay: AE, Disc, M, V, Checks
Parking: Yes
Handicap Access: Yes
Bar: Beer/wine
Hours: Daily 7am-9pm (Sa&Su 8am)

920 Town and Country Village
San Jose   408-244-5212

Well-suited for families with children and the college crowd, the no frills health-conscious meals are served three times a day, in generous portions, and come at the right price. Conveniently located in a shopping complex, the setting is comfy and casual. For breakfast try blueberry coffeecake or quesadillas. Later day offerings include soups, salads, sandwiches, burgers, and daily specials. See Quick-Check Table for highly-rated Mountain View and Palo Alto locations. (14 ratings/consistent)

Food	Service	Ambience	Value

| 82 | 71 | 72 | 71 |

Hong Kong Flower Lounge
Chinese $$$$

Reserv: Accepted
Dress: Informal
Pay: AE, DC, Disc, M, V
Parking: Yes
Handicap Access: Yes
Bar: Full/separate
Hours: M-F 11am-2:30pm, 5-10pm; Sa&Su 10am-2:30pm, 5-10:30pm

1671 El Camino Real
Millbrae   650-588-9972

Want your seafood fresh? You see it swimming in the tanks before it arrives at your table in this original that's perfect for family dining and serves authentic regional specialties. Known for its varied well-made dim sum and ample portions, the Peking duck is also recommended. Service can be distant and it's always packed, bustling, and noisy. See Quick-Check Table for highly-rated San Francisco and other Millbrae locations. (15 ratings/consistent)

| 85 | 59 | 50 | 84 |

House of Nanking
Chinese $

Reserv: Not accepted
Dress: Informal
Pay: Cash Only
Parking: No
Area: Chinatown
Handicap Access: Yes
Bar: Beer/wine
Hours: M-Sa 11am-10pm; Su 4-10pm

919 Kearny St
San Francisco   415-421-1429

This place is like a slap and a kiss at the same time. There's always a long line waiting to wedge into its sardine-can sized space and the service can be so bad it borders on offensive; so a visit here can be a letdown, except for a couple of things. One is the quality of dishes like Nanking scallops, sizzling-rice prawns, duck dumplings, Nanking chicken, and the daily house specials. The other is the cost—it's a steal. (16 ratings/mixed)

| 82 | 77 | 78 | 78 |

House of Prime Rib
Steak $$$$

Reserv: Suggested
Dress: Informal
Pay: AE, DC, M, V
Parking: Valet only
Area: Van Ness
Handicap Access: Yes
Bar: Full/separate
Hours: M-Th 5:30-10pm; F 5-10pm; Sa 4:30-10pm; Su 4-10pm

1906 Van Ness Ave
San Francisco   415-885-4605

"Outsized, American, carnivorous pleasure" (Unterman) awaits you at this half-century-old bastion that is great for multigenerational groups. Ordering here is easy—choose your cut of meat and type of potato, and the rest is up to them. First comes the chopped salad, then the cart laden with beef. The dining areas with overstuffed chairs, fireplaces, and hotel silver are Old-World comfortable. Service is professional. **Honors:** Unterman★★½ (33 ratings/consistent)

Food	Service	Ambience	Value

86 72 63 78 Hunan
Chinese $$

Reserv: Accepted
Dress: Informal
Pay: AE, DC, M, V
Parking: No
Area: North Beach
Handicap Access: Yes
Bar: Full
Hours: Daily 11:30am-9:30pm

924 Sansome
San Francisco   415-956-7727

Warehouse dining in a cavern-like setting that, despite its size, is always packed. You should expect hurried but personal service and out-of-this-world incendiary food—when the menu here says hot, believe it. Fortunately, they'll tailor everything to your personal liking. Raters recommend the chicken salad, Diana meat pie, curried chicken, hot and sour beef, and the "best dumplings anywhere." If you want less action, ask for a table in the back. (19 ratings/consistent)

80 76 74 73 Hungry Hunter
Steak $$$

Reserv: Accepted
Dress: Informal
Pay: AE, DC, Disc, M, V, Checks
Parking: Yes
Handicap Access: Ltd
Bar: Full/separate
Hours: M-F 11:30am-2pm, 5-10pm (F 10:30pm); Sa 5-10:30pm; Su 4-10pm

180 S Airport Blvd
S San Francisco   650-873-5131

The "hunter" stands true to its name by offering specialties that will appeal to famished carnivores, like 20-ounce slabs of prime rib or dinner-plate sized Porterhouse steaks, served in a native atmosphere of wildlife prints. For other members of the tribe there are surf-and-turf combos, seafood, chicken, and for lunch, sandwiches and salads. Best values are the early bird specials. See Quick-Check Table ratings for five other area locations. (15 ratings/consistent)

83 73 82 73 Iberia
Spanish $$$

Reserv: Suggested
Dress: Informal
Pay: AE, DC, M, V, Checks
Parking: Yes
Handicap Access: Ltd
Bar: Full/separate
Hours: Daily 11:30am-2:30pm, 5:30-10pm

190 Ladera-Alpine Rd
Portola Valley   650-854-1746

Enter these doors and you're in a rustic Alpine inn about to embark on a relaxed, romantic adventure of intoxicating aromas and fine regional specialties that some call expensive. Begin with gazpacho andaluz soup or fresh artichokes, then proceed on to the paella that's one of the best around, Garlician-style fish, or fabada asturiana (sausage and bean) casserole. Service is leisurely, but professional. Good selection of Spanish wines. Al fresco dining. (56 ratings/consistent)

Il Fornaio
Italian $$$

| 81 | 75 | 81 | 76 |

Reserv: Suggested
Dress: Informal
Pay: AE, DC, M. V
Parking: No
Handicap Access: Yes
Bar: Full
Hours: M-F 7-10:30am,
11:30am-11pm (F midnight);
Sa&Su 8am-11pm (Sa midnight)

302 S Market St
San Jose   408-271-3366

Raters just can't rave enough about the fabulous baked breads and pastries produced at this link in a chain that keeps multiplying. The menu includes some excellent pastas, like chicken conchiglie and lobster ravioli, a few pizzas, and full dinners. The interior is stylish with open spaces, high ceilings, a large fireplace, and comfortable seating. Weekend brunch. See Quick-Check Table ratings for Corte Madera, Palo Alto, and San Francisco locations. (33 ratings/mixed)

Iron Gate
Continental $$$$$

| 88 | 86 | 82 | 75 |

Reserv: Accepted
Dress: Informal
Pay: AE, DC, Disc, M, V
Parking: Yes
Handicap Access: Yes
Bar: Full/separate
Hours: M-F 11:30am-2:30pm;
M-Sa 5:30-10:30pm

1360 El Camino Real
Belmont   650-592-7893

This "longtime Peninsula favorite" has built a dedicated following on its "fresh and inviting setting" with "pleasant acoustics," excellent service, and "well-executed classics," often prepared tableside (Morgan). Top choices are the Caesar and Iron Gate salads, rack of lamb, steak Diane, veal piccata, and for dessert, standout soufflés. A separate bar has live piano music on weekends and a dance floor, if you're in the mood. (34 ratings/consistent)

Italian Colors
Italian $$$

| 80 | 82 | 74 | 82 |

Reserv: Accepted
Dress: Informal
Pay: AE, M, V
Parking: Yes
Area: Montclair Village
Handicap Access: Yes
Bar: Full
Hours: M-F 11:30am-2:30pm;
Daily 5:30-9:30pm

2220 Mountain Blvd
Oakland   510-482-8094

Raters praise this bustling neighborhood restaurant nestled in a hillside mini-mall for its good values and friendly service. The menu features salads, pasta, and pizzas. Try the green lasagna, smoked chicken salad, roasted chicken, and warm chocolate cake that's "worth the 15-minute wait" (Davis). The airy dining room is inviting and there is also al fresco dining with a fountain and colorful flowers. Live guitar on weekends. **Honors:** Davis (16 ratings/very consistent)

Food	Service	Ambience	Value

84 | 77 | 74 | 76 — Izzy's — *Steak* — $$$

Reserv: Suggested
Dress: Informal
Pay: AE, DC, Disc, M, V
Parking: Yes
Area: Marina
Handicap Access: Yes
Bar: Full/separate
Hours: Daily 5:30-10:30pm
(F&Sa 11pm)

3345 Steiner St
San Francisco   415-563-0487

Retro dining in a memorabilia-festooned fun joint that's always good. Steaks and chops can be near perfect, especially the New Yorks that "are worth falling off the wagon" for, but don't miss the top-notch loin lamb chops, peppered swordfish, and Maryland crab cakes. Recommended sides are potatoes and the creamed spinach. Though portions are generous, if you can manage it, cap everything off with a wedge of housemade key lime pie. Good for families. (22 ratings/consistent)

76 | 72 | 65 | 76 — Jade Villa — *Chinese* — $$

Reserv: Suggested weekends
Dress: Informal
Pay: M, V
Parking: No
Handicap Access: Yes
Bar: Beer/wine
Hours: Daily 9:30am-3pm

800 Broadway
Oakland   510-839-1688

You'll eat bountifully at this bustling dim sum house that, despite its 450-seat capacity, is always packed to the gills. The daytime draw is one of the biggest dim sum selections in the world and thrifty prices. Best dishes are the steamed dumplings, sesame balls, rice wrappers, and steamed prawns in the shell. Complaints about too much salt and grease can be eliminated by letting the teacarts carrying those items pass on by. Great for groups and children. (17 ratings/mixed)

83 | 74 | 60 | 81 — Jo Ann's Cafe — *Breakfast/Lunch* — $

Reserv: Not accepted
Dress: Informal
Pay: Cash Only
Parking: No
Area: Buri Buri District
Handicap Access: Yes
Bar: None
Hours: M-F 7:15am-2:30pm;
Sa&Su 8am-2:30pm

1131 El Camino Real
S San Francisco   650-872-2810

Everybody loves Jo Ann's for the meals that are better than those Mom used to make, and they're cheap beyond belief. Breakfast favorites include huevos Don Pasqual, create-your-own omelets, or berry hotcakes, when in season. Comfort lunches include BLT's, grilled chicken sandwiches, burgers, and several great salads. Seats are hard to get in this coffee shop/'40's diner, so expect a wait, especially on weekends. Breakfast and lunch only. (33 ratings/consistent)

73 **69** **68** **77**

Joe's of Westlake
Italian
$$

Reserv: Accepted
Dress: Informal
Pay: AE, M, V, Checks
Parking: Yes
Area: Westlake District
Handicap Access: Yes
Bar: Full/separate
Hours: Daily 11am-11pm
(F&Sa midnight)

11 Glenwood Ave
Daly City   650-755-7400

The Sinatra-martini crowd fits right into place in this clubby restaurant with a piano bar and candlelight dining. Many say there's "plenty of very good Italian food" here, with an accent on plenty, and recommend the scallops, huge burgers served on sourdough, veal scaloppine, New York steaks, and veal parmigiana. Others complain about the noise, the ever-present crowds, mediocre food, and long waits. Open late. (41 ratings/mixed)

---

83 **87** **88** **76**

John Ash & Co
California
$$$$

Reserv: Suggested
Dress: Informal
Pay: AE, M, V
Parking: Yes
Handicap Access: Yes
Bar: Full/separate
Hours: M 5:30-9pm; Tu-Sa
11:30am-2pm, 5:30-9pm;
Su 10:30am-2pm, 5:30-9pm

4330 Barnes Rd
Santa Rosa   707-527-7687

Forty-four acres of gorgeous vineyards set the scene for unsurpassed al fresco dining that epitomizes country elegance, with its superb but unobtrusive service and inspired menu that pays homage to the local bounty. With the influx of so many heavyweights nearby, the competition is keen and some find the prices here prohibitive. Sunday brunch. **Honors:** *Wine Spectator's* Best of Award of Excellence (18 ratings/very mixed)

---

86 **79** **77** **82**

Kabul
Afghan
$$

Reserv: Required
Dress: Informal
Pay: AE, M, V, Checks
Parking: Yes
Handicap Access: Yes
Bar: Beer/wine
Hours: M-F 11:30am-2pm,
5:30-10pm; Sa&Su 5:30-10pm

833 West El Camino Real
Sunnyvale   408-245-4350

"The lamb kabobs are the best!" along with the chicken, sauteed pumpkin, and a small but well-rounded menu of exotic specialties perfumed with aromatic spices. Start out with an order of aushak dumplings and don't miss the pallaw seasoned rice, or for stew, the challaw gulpi. Raters say the generous portions and comfortable, yet elegant, room settings make this an especially good value. See Quick-Check Table for highly-rated San Carlos location. (32 ratings/consistent)

| Food | Service | Ambience | Value |

83 78 91 82   Khan Toke Thai House $
Thai

Reserv: Suggested
Dress: Informal
Pay: AE, M, V
Parking: No
Area: Richmond
Handicap Access: Yes
Bar: Beer/wine
Hours: Daily 5-10:30pm

5937 Geary Blvd
San Francisco 415-668-6654

Leave your shoes at the door and enter a beautiful Thai temple with cushioned pillows, teak wall panels, and a garden with blooming flowers. Then allow the pleasant staff to bring you marvelous specialties like coconut chicken soup, squid with lemon grass, Thai crab, seafood curry, rice noodles, and fried bananas. If you're lucky enough to be dining on a Sunday evening, after suffering the inevitable wait for a table, expect to see live dancing as well. (13 ratings/mixed)

79 77 83 75   Kincaid's Bay House $$$$
Seafood

Reserv: Suggested
Dress: Informal
Pay: AE, DC, Disc, M, V, Checks
Parking: Valet only
Handicap Access: Yes
Bar: Full/separate
Hours: M-F 11:15am-10pm
(F 10:30pm); Sa 11:30am-
10:30pm; Su 10:30am-9pm

1 Franklin St
Oakland 510-835-8600

It's justifiably popular for its view of the Oakland estuary, honest drinks, sturdy food, unhurried atmosphere, and courteous service. The house prides itself on its corn-fed beef, Alaskan salmon, crab cakes, chicken, and pork; spit-roasted or broiled. For something out of the ordinary try the planked salmon. There is also a good selection of microbrews and Sunday brunch. See Quick-Check table ratings for Burlingame location. (39 ratings/consistent)

87 74 70 74   Kirala $$$
Japanese

Reserv: Not accepted
Dress: Informal
Pay: AE, M, V
Parking: No
Handicap Access: Yes
Bar: Beer/wine
Hours: M 5:30-9:30pm;
Tu-F 11:30am-1:45pm, 5:30-
9:30pm; Sa 5:30-9:30pm;
Su 5-9pm

2100 Ward St
Berkeley 510-549-3486

The popularity of this restaurant was established when it became one of the first with a robata grill and sushi bar. There's always a line out the door, even before it's opened, and the kudos keep coming in for the fresh sushi, perfectly grilled lobster, corn, and eggplant. The classics like tempura, udon noodles, or gyoza pot stickers are a cut above the norm. The spartan setting is offset by some lovely ceramics on the table.
Honors: Hamburg★★★ (29 ratings/consistent)

83 **78** **74** **84**

La Bergerie
French $$$

Reserv: Required
Dress: Informal
Pay: AE, Disc, M, V
Parking: No
Area: Richmond
Handicap Access: Yes
Bar: Beer/wine
Hours: Daily 5-10pm

4221 Geary Blvd
San Francisco   415-387-3573

With the '50's retro look coming back into style, the lime green vinyl banquettes overseen by a huge bust of Mozart make the setting here au courant again. But looks aren't the reason why it's been around for awhile. The true draw is the familiar, satisfying food that comes at reasonable prices. Escargots or rack of lamb, for example, are half the price you'd pay elsewhere, and the fixed-price meals are a steal, as are the thrifty wines. (16 ratings/consistent)

84 **78** **81** **76**

La Cocotte
French $$$

Reserv: Suggested
Dress: Informal
Pay: AE, DC, Disc, M, V, Checks
Parking: Yes
Handicap Access: Yes
Bar: Beer/wine
Hours: Daily 5:30-10:30pm

6115 Main St
Clayton   925-672-1333

This friendly neighborhood hideaway clearly has a fan club. Yes, the food is similar to what you see on a menu of yesteryear—frog's legs, sweetbreads, duck with orange, and veal in mustard sauce, but each is prepared with finesse. Furthermore, the dinner includes soup, salad, and dessert, and you don't have to empty your wallet to dine well. House favorites include poached salmon, lamb fillets, and veal oscar. Family-owned and operated, expect personal service. Outdoor dining. (13 ratings/consistent)

80 **76** **75** **78**

La Creme de la Creme
French $$

Reserv: Suggested
Dress: Informal
Pay: AE, M, V, Checks
Parking: No
Handicap Access: No
Bar: Beer/wine
Hours: M 5:30-9pm; Tu-Sa 11:30am-2pm, 5:30-9pm; Su 9am-2pm, 5:30-9pm

5362 College Ave
Oakland   510-420-8822

This quaint charming cottage, a neighborhood favorite, has a lovely courtyard for al fresco meals. The large menu provides a host of rustic country specialties, but their execution gets only mixed reviews from raters. Among the best are the pastas, braised lamb with vegetables, oven-broiled game hens, and the superb chocolate gateau. Homemade breads baked on the premises are also recommended, especially for Sunday brunch. **Honors:** Crum B-/B+ (33 ratings/mixed)

Food **Service** **Ambience** **Value**

La Fiesta
Mexican $$

Reserv: Suggested
Dress: Informal
Pay: AE, M, V
Parking: Yes
Handicap Access: Yes
Bar: Full/separate
Hours: M-F 11am-2pm, 5-9pm
(F 10pm); Sa&Su 11am-3pm,
5-10pm (Su 9pm)

240 Villa St
Mountain View   650-968-1364

Choose from over 100 tequilas and join the party at this colorful cucina that's known for its great margaritas, casual atmosphere, and good food. House specialties include mole poblano (chicken simmered in a spicy cocoa bean sauce), chimichangas, camarones picante (shrimp sauteed in a guajillo and chipotle sauce), and chiles colorado or verde. Large portions and thrifty prices help sweeten the deal. Weekend brunch. Outdoor dining. (24 ratings/consistent)

La Folie
French $$$$$

Reserv: Suggested
Dress: Informal
Pay: AE, DC, Disc, M, V
Parking: Valet only
Area: Russian Hill
Handicap Access: Yes
Bar: Full
Hours: M-Sa 5:30-10pm

2316 Polk St
San Francisco   415-776-5577

The stellar food here "is every bit as refined as anyone's in town," (Bauer) and though expensive, a meal here can be "exhilarating"(Miller). For best values order from the nightly fixed price menu. Look for the goat cheese tatin, "exceptional" duck, and "standout" roti of quail and squab (Miller). Recent remodeling has formalized the whimsical but cramped setting. Service can be weak. **Honors:** Bauer★★★, Miller A-/B+ (26 ratings/consistent)

La Mediterranee
Middle Eastern $

Reserv: Not accepted
Dress: Informal
Pay: AE, DC, M, V, Checks
Parking: No
Handicap Access: Yes
Bar: Beer/wine
Hours: M-Sa 10am-10pm
(F&Sa 11pm)

2936 College Ave
Berkeley   510-540-7773

The exceptional values probably explain why it is always crowded, but all agree it's worth the wait. Popular appetizers are hummus, baba ghanoush, and tabuleh. For entrees, the middle eastern plates offer several specialties, and the chicken pomegranate is a true spice adventure. The cafe space is pretty cramped, so dine outdoors if you want to stretch. Friendly service. Brunch on weekends. (13 ratings/consistent)

Food	Service	Ambience	Value

84 79 79 74 | ### La Pastaia—De Anza Hotel **$$$**
Italian

Reserv: Suggested
Dress: Informal
Pay: AE, M, V
Parking: No
Handicap Access: Yes
Bar: Full
Hours: M-F 11am-3pm, 5-10pm (F 10:30pm); Sa&Su noon-2pm, 5-10:30pm (Su 9pm)

233 W Santa Clara St
San Jose 408-286-8686

Opera music, slick neo-Etruscan design, and a cappuccino bar pair up with contemporary pastas, pizzas, and several inspired entrees to make this hotel restaurant popular. High marks go to entrees such as osso bucco, grilled pork stuffed with apples and sage, polenta, and roasted chicken with apricots. Some raters grouse about difficult parking and excessive noise, but the atmosphere, large portions, and broad menu make the place good for groups. Outdoor dining. (29 ratings/mixed)

---

75 71 74 78 | ### La Pinata **$$**
Mexican

Reserv: Not accepted
Dress: Informal
Pay: AE, DC, Disc, M, V
Parking: Yes
Handicap Access: Yes
Bar: Full/separate
Hours: Daily 11:30am-10pm (F&Sa 11pm)

1205 Burlingame Ave
Burlingame 650-375-1070

Pokey the parrot greets you at the door of this festive taqueria decorated with street scene murals, swinging pinatas, and a lively bar abuzz with blenders making margaritas. The real draws here are the top-notch ingredients carefully used to prepare the huge portions of enchiladas, chile rellenos, carnitas, and pollo al mesquite that come with "outstanding refried beans" (Morgan). Low prices help to offset occasional waits for tables. **Honors:** Morgan★★ (13 ratings/mixed)

---

85 76 63 89 | ### La Taqueria **$**
Mexican

Reserv: Not accepted
Dress: Informal
Pay: Cash Only
Parking: No
Area: Mission
Handicap Access: Yes
Bar: Beer
Hours: Daily 11am-9pm (Su 8pm)

2889 Mission St
San Francisco 415-285-7117

Incredible dining values are offered at this tidy self-service taqueria where the ingredients begin fresh and end up tasting great. The streamlined menu features tacos, burritos, and quesadillas, but you choose among 13 fillings including chunky chicken, simmered pork, chorizo, and grilled beef, then add from a substantial list of condiments. Don't miss the homemade aguas frescas made from fresh fruit. Not much in the way of ambience but outdoor seating is available. (14 ratings/consistent)

| Food | Service | Ambience | Value |

83 **81** **74** **74** **Laghi** $$$
Italian

Reserv: Suggested
Dress: Informal
Pay: AE, DC, M, V
Parking: No
Area: Richmond
Handicap Access: Yes
Bar: Full/separate
Hours: Daily 5-11pm

1801 Clement St
San Francisco   415-386-6266

What's cozy to some is cramped to others, and parking
may be a problem, but this simple cafe offers luxury
dining at affordable prices. The small menu that
changes daily features regional country-style specialties
made from scratch. Look for polenta, mushroom or
truffle risotto, ragouts of duck and venison, and
"tiramisu to die for." Be sure to say hello to the
chef/owner; he likes to mingle and make sure everyone
is happy and satisfied. (18 ratings/mixed)

---

84 **80** **76** **79** **Lalime's** $$$
Mediterranean

Reserv: Suggested
Dress: Informal
Pay: M, V, Checks
Parking: No
Handicap Access: Yes
Bar: Beer/wine
Hours: M-Sa 5:30-9:30pm
(F&Sa 10pm); Su 5-9pm

1329 Gilman St
Berkeley   510-527-9838

The reputation of this neighborhood spot that serves
inventive dishes in a charming setting hasn't faltered
since it opened years ago. Nor has the format for the
menu that changes every two days. There is a creative a
la carte menu, plus a three-course fixed price special
that's the "best bang for the buck," and for which this
place is known. Excellent desserts are a hallmark.
Monthly mailings let you plan in advance.
Honors: Boer A/A (85 ratings/consistent)

---

83 **80** **84** **73** **Lark Creek Inn** $$$$
California

Reserv: Suggested
Dress: Informal
Pay: AE, DC, M, V
Parking: Yes
Handicap Access: Yes
Bar: Full/separate
Hours: M-F 11:30am-2pm,
5-8:45pm; Sa 5-10pm; Su 10am-
2pm, 5-9pm

234 Magnolia Ave
Larkspur   415-924-7766

The creekside setting amidst a redwood grove,
polished oak floors, linen-covered tables, and
innovative regional cuisine that can be costly keep this
elegant Victorian packed with patrons. Best bets include
pot roast, short ribs, ravioli, and butterscotch pudding.
To avoid the crowds, go midweek. Al fresco dining is
nice for Sunday brunch. **Honors:** *Focus* Best North
Bay, Unterman★★★, *Wine Spectator*'s Award of
Excellence (79 ratings/consistent)

80 **84** **77** **73**

Le Central
French

$$$$

Reserv: Required
Dress: Informal
Pay: AE, DC, M, V
Parking: No
Area: Union Square
Handicap Access: Yes
Bar: Full
Hours: M-Sa 11:30am-
10:30pm

453 Bush St
San Francisco   415-391-2233

The Left Bank thrives in this authentic, rustic brasserie
where the bigwigs meet. Though some critics
complain that it's passé, the menu is rich in the comforting classics: cassoulet, roasted chicken, choucroute
alsacienne, and filet mignon with "fantastic pommes
frites." The interior fits the part perfectly with bentwood
cafe chairs, a zinc bar, bistro tables, and art posters.
Service can be professional but sometimes aloof.
(16 ratings/mixed)

77 **78** **69** **79**

Le Chalet Basque
Basque

$$

Reserv: Suggested
Dress: Informal
Pay: AE, Disc, M, V
Parking: Yes
Handicap Access: Yes
Bar: Full/separate
Hours: Tu-Sa 11am-2pm,
5-10pm

405 N San Pedro Rd
San Rafael   415-479-1070

Basque at its best that never deviates from near
excellence marks this long-standing favorite as a place
raters can't forget. The food here is comforting, rich
and reminiscent of a bygone era: sweetbreads, veal,
prawns a la provencal, and lamb. The ambience is a
perfect match with lace curtains, flowered wallpaper,
and French-speaking waitstaff. Come here when you're
hungry and want to linger—dinner comes with five
courses. Outdoor dining. (14 ratings/consistent)

86 **81** **75** **87**

Le Charm
Bistro

$$

Reserv: Required
Dress: Informal
Pay: AE, M, V
Parking: No
Area: South of Market
Handicap Access: Yes
Bar: Beer/wine
Hours: M-F 11:30am-2pm,
6-9:30pm; Sa 5:30-10pm

315 5th St
San Francisco   415-546-6128

A tiny oasis of great food and incredible bargains in a
gritty part of town, this is one of the city's best-kept
secrets. Fixed-price dinners are about half the price
you'd pay elsewhere. The atmosphere is informal with
patio dining, and because of the unusual location, it's
always packed with an eclectic mix of people. Try the
chicken liver salad, escargots, duck confit, or tarte
Tatin and you'll become a regular too.
Honors: Cianci★★½ (21 ratings/consistent)

77	70	65	80

Le Cheval
Vietnamese $$

Reserv: Suggested
Dress: Informal
Pay: AE, DC, Disc, M, V
Parking: Yes (after 5pm)
Handicap Access: Yes
Bar: Full
Hours: M-Sa 11am-9:30pm;
Su 5-9:30pm

1007 Clay St
Oakland 510-763-8495

Though the name sounds French, the food here is purely Vietnamese with intriguing sauces, exceptionally fresh vegetables, and some of the area's most enticing deals, though some raters aren't impressed. Start with an order of shrimp or pork rolls, then work your way into the grilled kebabs, spicy orange beef, watercress salad, or lemon grass specialties. Substantial portions and efficient service make this great for groups and business lunches. (26 ratings/mixed)

80	74	72	81

Le Cyrano
French $$$

Reserv: Suggested
Dress: Informal
Pay: M, V
Parking: No
Area: Richmond
Handicap Access: Ltd
Bar: Full
Hours: M-Sa 5-10pm; Su 4:30-9pm

4134 Geary Blvd
San Francisco 415-387-1090

This is the kind of place where things haven't changed in three decades because they haven't needed to. Regulars keep coming here for the classics that fuel fond memories: frog's legs, escargots, coquille St. Jacques, rack of lamb, and chocolate mousse—dishes that are outdated to some, but comforting and satisfying to others. The atmosphere is quaint with chandeliers, tied curtains, and intimate candlelight. Prices are very reasonable. (19 ratings/very mixed)

86	85	71	89

Le Maconnais
French $$$$

Reserv: Suggested
Dress: Informal
Pay: AE, M, V, Checks
Parking: Yes
Handicap Access: Ltd
Bar: Beer/wine
Hours: Tu-F 11:30am-2pm,
5-9pm (F 9:30pm); Sa&Su 5-9:30pm (Su 9pm)

21181 Foothill Blvd
Hayward 510-538-3522

Take a little house in an out-of-the-way location, furnish it with yellow upholstery, chandeliers, and velvet drapes, then serve outstanding food at reasonable prices and you have an undiscovered jewel that garners the silver medal for unbelievable bargains in the Bay Area. House specials include duck with lingonberries and port-orange sauce, veal with wild mushrooms, and salmon in papillote. Service is personal and attentive. Outdoor dining. (14 ratings/consistent)

Food	Service	Ambience	Value

| 85 | 86 | 81 | 77 |

Le Marquis
French　$$$

Reserv: Required
Dress: Informal
Pay: M, V
Parking: Yes
Handicap Access: Ltd
Bar: Full
Hours: Tu-F 11:30am-2pm,
5-10pm; Sa&Su 5-10pm

3524-B Mt Diablo Blvd
Lafayette   925-284-4422

Cognac, wine tastings, cigars, live jazz, and al fresco dining have been added to this venerable heavyweight that, for its 20th anniversary, lightened its look to appeal to younger patrons. Standards are still high, and service is solicitous and professional but the biggest change is in the menu that infuses eclectic California cooking with N.Y. bistro style in a creative, outstanding manner. Try the sunset specials if the prices seem high. Outdoor dining. (14 ratings/mixed)

| 86 | 82 | 85 | 73 |

Le Mouton Noir
French　$$$$$

Reserv: Suggested
Dress: Informal
Pay: AE, DC, M, V
Parking: Yes
Handicap Access: Yes
Bar: Full
Hours: Sa 11:30am-2pm;
Daily 5-9pm

14560 Big Basin Way
Saratoga   408-867-7017

Raters' comments teeter on the extremes for this long-lived favorite that's heralded by the critics. Everyone seems to agree that the quaint Victorian setting is a tremendous asset, as is the excellent service. The rift seems to center on the food which, to some, "is to die for" (Himmel) while to others, is plagued by odd tasting combinations at a high cost. A daily fixed price menu and Saturday brunch are offered. Outdoor dining.
Honors: Himmel★★★ (27 ratings/mixed)

| 93 | 91 | 92 | 81 |

Le Papillon
French　$$$$$

Reserv: Suggested
Dress: Informal
Pay: AE, DC, Disc, M, V
Parking: Yes
Handicap Access: Yes
Bar: Full
Hours: M-F 11:30am-2:30pm;
Daily 5-10pm

410 Saratoga Ave
San Jose   408-296-3730

Awarding extremely high scores across the board, raters rave about the unbelievable food, perfect service, incredible setting, and astronomical prices at this Silicon Valley hot spot. The setting is tastefully under-stated and both regular and fixed price menus (offering the best deals) are available for lunch and dinner. Specialties include wild game, fish, and veal, paired with a variety of exotic ingredients.
Honors: Himmel★★★½ (20 ratings/consistent)

83	85	79	81

Le Petit Bistro
Bistro $$$$

Reserv: Suggested
Dress: Informal
Pay: AE, Checks
Parking: Yes
Handicap Access: Yes
Bar: Beer/wine
Hours: Tu-Su 5-10pm

1405 West El Camino Real
Mountain View   650-964-3321

A charming, unpretentious bistro with a small, but well-rounded menu. Though the ratings are mixed, most comment favorably on owner/chef Jean Michel's superb delicacy with sauces and recommend the fixed-price specials to keep the bill down. House favorites include amply proportioned bowls of steamed mussels, vegetarian crepes, rabbit, and cassoulet. Service gets high marks for being friendly and adept. The only complaint: small portions for some items. (21 ratings/mixed)

83	78	75	83

Lemon Grass
Thai $

Reserv: Suggested
Dress: Informal
Pay: AE, DC, M, V, Checks
Parking: No
Handicap Access: Yes
Bar: Beer
Hours: M-Sa 11am-3:30pm,
5-9:30pm; Su 4-9:30pm

2216 1st St
Livermore   925-606-6496

With its painted landscape murals, native handcrafts, and waitstaff donned in Thai costumes, this unusual eating spot could pass for a stage set from "The King and I," but the true draw here is the comprehensive menu. Try the tom-ka-gai chicken soup, grilled salmon, and fried bananas, with a glass of Thai iced tea. The only downside raters report is an unchanging menu—but why reinvent the wheel when it already works so well? (15 ratings/mixed)

73	77	68	76

Line-Up
Mexican $$$

Reserv: Suggested
Dress: Informal
Pay: AE, M, V
Parking: No
Area: South of Market
Handicap Access: Yes
Bar: Full/separate
Hours: Daily 11am-11pm

398 7th
San Francisco   415-861-2887

There's a double draw at this neighborhood Victorian favorite: the drinks and the food. Many come here just for the strawberry margaritas, chips, and salsa. Others like to settle down to a plate full of the mainland classics—tacos, crab enchiladas, and mole. Sunday buffet brunch is fun and the friendly setting is convenient for a business lunch. Service is good, and prices are reasonable. (23 ratings/consistent)

Food	Service	Ambience	Value

78 **74** **71** **76** | ### Little City Antipasti Bar $$$
Mediterranean

Reserv: Suggested
Dress: Informal
Pay: AE, M, V
Parking: Yes
Area: North Beach
Handicap Access: Yes
Bar: Full
Hours: M-Sa 11:30am-4pm,
5-11pm (F&Sa midnight);
Su 10:30am-3pm, 5-11pm

673 Union St
San Francisco 415-434-2900

Sample a huge assortment of small antipasti plates, some of which date back a decade or two, and a few pastas, salads, and entrees in this comfortable brick eatery with a view of Washington Square. The action-packed bar offers a large selection of wines and is great for people watching. Live music on certain evenings, Sunday brunch, and late hours add to the amenities, but the biggest draw is the upbeat atmosphere. Outdoor dining. (13 ratings/consistent)

69 **64** **52** **77** | ### Long Life Vegi House $
Vegetarian

Reserv: Suggested
Dress: Informal
Pay: AE, Disc, M, V
Parking: No
Handicap Access: Yes
Bar: Beer/wine
Hours: Daily 11:30am-9:30pm

2129 University Ave
Berkeley 510-845-6072

Wonderful, cheap food in a depressing barn-like setting, diners come here for the exclusive menu that features seafood and vegetables only—the kind of place your doctor would love. Look for the vegi-chicken on lotus leaf (made with mock poultry), and eggplant with spicy garlic sauce. Though some raters comment on a recent downhill trend here and poor service, at these prices you feel guilty complaining. Dim sum on weekends. (16 ratings/mixed)

78 **75** **74** **75** | ### Lou's Village $$$$
Seafood

Reserv: Suggested
Dress: Informal
Pay: AE, DC, Disc, M, V
Parking: Yes
Handicap Access: Yes
Bar: Full
Hours: M-F 11:30am-3pm,
4-10pm; Sa&Su 4:30-10pm

1465 W San Carlos
San Jose 408-293-4570

If history was taken into account, this oldie but goodie would win hands down for its past lives as a nightclub, outdoor barbecue, and political meeting place. Today it's a seafood restaurant with banquet facilities for a thousand—a cross between a warehouse and a convention center that serves mostly surf, or surf 'n turf combos that win only mixed reviews. The best bet here is the lobster or the lobster thermidor that comes fresh from the nearby tanks. (17 ratings/mixed)

Food	Service	Ambience	Value

86 | 86 | 78 | 86   Luzern $$$
French/Swiss

Reserv: Suggested
Dress: Informal
Pay: M, V, Checks
Parking: No
Area: Sunset
Handicap Access: Yes
Bar: Beer/wine
Hours: W-Su 5-10pm

1429 Noriega St
San Francisco   415-664-2353

When a restaurant serves the same menu for a quarter century and is still popular, you know it has something going for it. Raters' praises for this homey place are unilateral: delicious food, an intimate atmosphere, warm and friendly service, and good values. The food is rich and enduring: wienerschnitzel, sweetbreads, beef fondue, veal with morels, coquille St. Jacques. Moderate prices are best at lunch.
(29 ratings/consistent)

71 | 67 | 66 | 77   Lyon's $$
American

Reserv: Not accepted
Dress: Informal
Pay: AE, Disc, M, V
Parking: Yes
Handicap Access: Ltd
Bar: Full/separate
Hours: Daily 24 hours

1750 N Main St
Walnut Creek   925-935-4666

Coffee shop dining thrives at this local favorite that's open 24 hours a day. Slip into the cocktail lounge for a cool margarita, or if you're hungry, slide into a booth or find a counter seat where the coffee's always hot. Then try one of the classics like a burger, tuna melt, chicken-fried steak, or liver and onions, with a milkshake on the side. Great for multigenerational dining. Weekend brunch. See Quick-Check Table rating for San Mateo location. (20 ratings/consistent)

73 | 66 | 68 | 75   Maharani $$$
Indian

Reserv: Suggested
Dress: Informal
Pay: AE, DC, Disc, M, V, Checks
Parking: No
Handicap Access: Yes
Bar: Beer/wine
Hours: Daily 11:30am-9pm

1025 University Ave
Berkeley   510-848-7777

While the food here strikes some as "the best in the universe," others disagree and grumble about sparse, rude service that needs to be improved. But when the cards are down, everyone seems to appreciate the fixed-price buffet lunches that feature unlimited quantities of such items as chicken tandoori, lamb curry, and salmon marsala. Diners still leave with plenty of change to spare. Interesting artifacts add to the sense of the exotic. (16 ratings/mixed)

Food	Service	Ambience	Value

| 80 | 71 | 63 | 74 |

Mama Lan's $$
Vietnamese

Reserv: Suggested
Dress: Informal
Pay: M, V
Parking: No
Handicap Access: Ltd
Bar: Beer/wine
Hours: M-Sa 11am-3pm, 5-9:30pm

1316 Gilman St
Berkeley 510-528-1790

Neighborhood dining doesn't get much better than at this simple corner spot that's so tiny you can hear them cooking your meal. The big draws here are the crab and seafood, although other specialties shouldn't be overlooked. For a flavor-packed meal order the stir-fried crab, the Vietnamese crepe that's sublime, and the fresh and crisp Goi Cuon rice paper rolls. Other hits include the garlic catfish, gargantuan springrolls, and green papaya salad. (13 ratings/consistent)

| 76 | 71 | 67 | 78 |

Mandalay $
Burmese

Reserv: Suggested
Dress: Informal
Pay: M, V
Parking: No
Area: Richmond
Handicap Access: Yes
Bar: Beer/wine
Hours: Daily 11:30am-9:30pm

4348 California
San Francisco 415-386-3895

This storefront restaurant is a good choice when you want something out of the ordinary and don't care about the decor. Although the menu is diverse, stick to the Burmese offerings for best results. Raters recommend the incredible Lop Pad Bok—tea salad tossed tableside. Other attractions include the ginger salad, coconut chicken soup, fish chowder, Mandalay squid, and mango chicken. (18 ratings/mixed)

| 82 | 78 | 83 | 72 |

Mandarin Gourmet $$$
Chinese

Reserv: Suggested
Dress: Informal
Pay: AE, M, V
Parking: No
Handicap Access: Yes
Bar: Full/separate
Hours: M-Sa 11:30am-2:30pm, 5-10pm; Su 5-9:30pm

420 Ramona St
Palo Alto 650-328-8898

Attention to detail is important here making this peninsula favorite a cut above the norm—just check out the way they fold napkins and mu shu wrappers. The setting is sleek and clean and many dishes are prepared tableside for a flourish of elegance and theatrics. House favorites include chicken salad, prawns with honeyed walnuts, orange beef, and smoked duck. (29 ratings/consistent)

Food Service Ambience Value

84	69	74	64

Manka's Inverness Lodge $$$$
California

Reserv: Accepted
Dress: Informal
Pay: M, V, Checks
Parking: Yes
Handicap Access: No
Bar: Beer/wine
Hours: M,Th,F 6-9pm; Sa 5:30-9pm; Su 5:30-8:30pm

30 Callendar
Inverness   415-669-1034

A trip to this rustic hunting lodge hidden in the woods is a romantic step back in time. Elegant crisp linens offset rough-hewn timbered ceilings and walls. The fires are ablaze, some of them roasting the game specialties for the day. House cured pork chops, venison, wild boar sausage, duck, and local fresh seafood grilled over the open pits are house specialties. Even with a fixed-price menu, prices are high. Live jazz certain Sundays. (18 ratings/consistent)

76	76	72	80

Marie Callender's $$
American

Reserv: Suggested
Dress: Informal
Pay: AE, Disc, M, V, Checks
Parking: Yes
Handicap Access: Yes
Bar: Full/separate
Hours: M-Sa 8am-10pm (F&Sa 11pm); Su 9am-10pm

620 Blossom Hill Rd
San Jose   408-578-0643

A trip here is like a visit to grandma's house and feasting on heartland classics. Breakfast and Sunday buffet brunch feature omelets, waffles, eggs, and a variety of baked items. Lunch brings on soups and salads. Dinner highlights like meatloaf, pasta, burgers, and pot roast provide sustenance before you launch into one of their legendary pies. Thrifty prices make it a family favorite. See Quick-Check Table ratings for four other area locations. (14 ratings/very consistent)

87	90	83	69

Masa's $$$$$
French

Reserv: Required
Dress: Coat/tie required
Pay: AE, DC, Disc, M, V, Checks
Parking: Valet only
Area: Union Square
Handicap Access: Yes
Bar: Full
Hours: Tu-Sa 6-9:30pm

648 Bush St
San Francisco   415-989-7154

Recent remodeling has given new gusto to professional critics' praises, but our raters say a meal here can be hit or miss. Some complain that the daily fixed-price menu is too limited and too expensive. Still, price aside, most agree the Maine lobster salad, fallow deer, and foie gras are incredible, and the setting and service luxuriant. **Honors:** *Focus* Best, *Gourmet*, *Wine Spectator*'s Best of Award of Excellence (30 ratings/mixed)

Food	Service	Ambience	Value

83 | 79 | 80 | 79

Massimo's
Italian $$$$

Reserv: Suggested
Dress: Informal
Pay: AE, DC, Disc, M, V
Parking: Yes
Handicap Access: Yes
Bar: Full/separate
Hours: M-F 11:30am-3pm,
5-10pm; Sa 5-10pm

5200 Mowry
Fremont   510-792-2000

Tired of trendy cuisine? This place shouts continental
dining of an era when booths, chandeliers, and
tableside service were in vogue. Choose the excellent
Caesar salad, minestrone, rack of lamb, crab and
spaghetti, or veal picatta: all done in the traditional way.
Service too has that air of gracious efficiency. If you're
in the mood for some action, order cherries jubilee or
bananas foster for a flaming and memorable conclusion
to your meal. Outdoor dining. (15 ratings/consistent)

76 | 73 | 71 | 78

Max's
American $$$

Reserv: Suggested
Dress: Informal
Pay: AE, DC, Disc, M, V
Parking: Yes
Handicap Access: Yes
Bar: Full
Hours: M-F 11:30am-10pm (F
11pm); Sa&Su 10am-11pm (Su
10pm)

1001 El Camino Real
Redwood City   650-365-6297

And yet another place where Max and his cohorts have
hung up a shingle and started serving good taste and
big servings to the throngs who clamor after New York
deli fare. The theme is still "more than you can eat" so
expect gargantuan corned beef reubens, huge double
stuffed potatoes, and bathtub-sized bowls of matzo ball
soup, and don't worry—Max buys doggie bags by the
gross. Outdoor dining. See Quick-Check Table ratings
for other area locations. (17 ratings/mixed)

80 | 78 | 72 | 80

Max's Opera Cafe
American $$$

Reserv: Accepted
Dress: Informal
Pay: AE, DC, Disc, M, V
Parking: No
Handicap Access: Yes
Bar: Full/separate
Hours: M-F 11:30am-10pm
(F 11pm); Sa&Su 10am-11pm
(Su 10pm)

1676 N California Blvd
Walnut Creek   925-932-3434

"The best Jewish deli this side of the Hudson River,"
with a singing waitstaff, a broad menu, and trough-sized
portions. Besides the mile-high reubens and potted
briskets, you'll find steaks, BBQ, burgers, pasta, and
daily specials. And for those who don't know when
enough is enough, there are larger-than-life desserts. After
6pm you'll be serenaded by waiters hoping to make it to
the Met. Outdoor dining. See Quick-Check Table ratings
for other area locations. (60 ratings/consistent)

Food	Service	Ambience	Value

Mifune
Japanese
$$

Reserv: Not accepted
Dress: Informal
Pay: AE, DC, Disc, M, V
Parking: No
Area: Japantown
Handicap Access: Yes
Bar: Beer/wine
Hours: Daily 11am-9:30pm
(F&Sa 10pm)

1737 Post
San Francisco   415-922-0337

No trip to Japantown is complete without a stop here.
First choose your noodles: either white (udon) or buck-
wheat (soba); then figure out whether you want them
hot or cold; then decide what you want in them. What
you get is a bowl of the best noodles ever, and one of
the best values around. The decor is stark, but clean,
and diners slip into booths where, as the menu insists,
"it's OK to slurp your noodles!" (16 ratings/mixed)

Miraku
Japanese
$$$

Reserv: Suggested
Dress: Informal
Pay: AE, DC, Disc, M, V
Parking: Yes
Handicap Access: Yes
Bar: Full
Hours: M-F 11:30am-2:30pm;
Daily 5-9:30pm (F&Sa 10pm)

3740 Mt Diablo Blvd
Lafayette   925-284-5700

The kitchen of this neighborhood favorite is deft in its
handling of seafood used for the excellent sushi and for
full-fledged dinners. Besides sushi, house favorites
include sashimi, chicken, salmon, and beef teriyaki. In
keeping with the sophisticated and serene setting with
bleached wood chairs and slate carpet, a large selection
of premium sakes is featured. Outdoor dining. See
Quick-Check Table ratings for Walnut Creek location.
(14 ratings/consistent)

Mistral
California/Mediterranean
$$$

Reserv: Suggested
Dress: Informal
Pay: AE, DC, M, V
Parking: Yes
Handicap Access: Yes
Bar: Full
Hours: M-F 11:30am-10pm;
Sa&Su 5:30-10pm (Su 9pm)

370-6 Bridge Pkwy
Redwood City   650-802-9222

You're surrounded by the elements in this airy, open
restaurant that looks out onto a bayside lagoon. Inside
crackles a wood-fired oven used for baking creative
specialties like fresh baked salmon, an assortment of
unusual pizzas, teriyaki steak, and homemade pasta. To
escape the crowds and noise, raters say the best seats in
the house are on the patio where the views are unsur-
passed. Good selection of wines. **Honors:** *Wine
Spectator*'s Award of Excellence (17 ratings/consistent)

Food	Service	Ambience	Value

74 | 57 | 57 | 77 — Mom Is Cooking $
Mexican

Reserv: Suggested
Dress: Informal
Pay: Cash Only
Parking: Yes
Area: Excelsior
Handicap Access: Yes
Bar: Full/separate
Hours: Daily noon-2pm.
3-10pm

1166 Geneva Ave
San Francisco   415-586-7000

This out-of-the-way place has built a huge following despite raters' very mixed opinions that range from "the best Mexican food we've ever eaten" to "mediocre." Regulars come for the layered boquitos appetizer, tamales, mole con pollo, enchiladas, and potpurri Mexicano. Others say the funky setting with red Naugahyde booths patched with Astroturf, and the 60 types of tequila are worth the trip alone. Patio dining. (17 ratings/very mixed)

85 | 79 | 72 | 82 — Montecatini $$
Italian

Reserv: Required
Dress: Informal
Pay: AE, M, V
Parking: Yes
Handicap Access: Yes
Bar: Full/separate
Hours: Tu-Sa 5-10pm (F&Sa
10:30pm); Su 5-9:30pm

1528 Civic Dr
Walnut Creek   925-943-6608

A terrific place for those who want both good food and a good time; come here for crisp salads, comforting pastas, high quality grilled meats, and homemade desserts—all prepared in the classic manner. House specialties include grilled and sauteed seafood, veal or chicken piccata, gnocchi, and fettucine carbonara. Waiters are efficient and well-informed, and the ambience is unpretentious and casual. The only drawback is the noise. (14 ratings/mixed)

82 | 79 | 81 | 74 — Moose's $$$
California/Mediterranean

Reserv: Suggested
Dress: Informal
Pay: AE, DC, M, V
Parking: Valet
Area: North Beach
Handicap Access: Yes
Bar: Full/separate
Hours: M-Sa 11:30am-11pm
(F&Sa midnight); Su 9:30am-
11pm

1652 Stockton
San Francisco   415-989-7800

The swinging San Francisco scene is happening at this lively, feel-good place where there's always a crowd and a celebrity or two. The "huge roaring room" (Unterman), with a bustling bar and live jazz provides a backdrop for the hearty fare with excellent salads and protein-rich entrees like spaghetti arrabiata, Mooseburgers, and marinated chicken. Sunday brunch. **Honors:** Bauer★★½, *Gourmet*, Unterman★★½, *Wine Spectator*'s Award of Excellence (47 ratings/consistent)

Food	Service	Ambience	Value		

83 **77** **76** **76**

Mustards Grill
American

$$$

Reserv: Suggested
Dress: Informal
Pay: DC, Disc, M, V
Parking: Yes
Area: North of Yountville
Handicap Access: Yes
Bar: Full
Hours: Daily 11:30am-9:30pm

7399 St Helena Hwy
Napa   707-944-2424

The notion of a classic road house grill reaches new heights at this popular place that has reinvented American cuisine. The menu features classics like ribs, onion rings, and burgers, right alongside tea-smoked duck, tandoori chicken, and Mongolian pork—for those who want it contemporary and have ample pocketbooks. The service and setting are relaxed and casual, but the convivial atmosphere is sometimes too noisy. (58 ratings/mixed)

83 **73** **70** **76**

Nadine
Continental

$$

Reserv: Suggested
Dress: Informal
Pay: M, V, Checks
Parking: No
Handicap Access: Yes
Bar: Beer/wine
Hours: Tu-F 11:30am-2pm;
Daily 5:30-9pm

4228 Park Blvd
Oakland   510-482-5303

This neighborhood favorite has a solid following of locals who come for the intimate bistro setting and high quality food. On the small but excellent menu you'll find several inspired continental specialties like an earthy beet salad with feta and caramelized garlic, Hungarian goulash, salmon encrusted in fennel, and a chunky seafood risotto. The atmosphere receives a touch of Bohemia with contemporary art and gracious service. (16 ratings/very consistent)

82 **77** **69** **81**

Nan Yang Rockridge
Burmese

$$

Reserv: Suggested
Dress: Informal
Pay: M, V
Parking: No
Handicap Access: Ltd
Bar: Beer/wine
Hours: Tu-Sa 11:30am-10pm;
Su noon-9:30pm

6048 College Ave
Oakland   510-655-3298

Exotic value-laden dining is only as far as a trip through the doors of this sleek, contemporary spot that brought the pleasures of the South Pacific to the Bay Area. Among them are complex salads like the crisp ginger and the green tea, chicken curry soup, the 24 types of garlic noodles, five-spice chicken, exotic curries, or mango prawns. Service is friendly but sometimes rushed when they're overwhelmed by excessive business. Patio dining. (21 ratings/consistent)

73 **71** **71** **79**

New Rochelle
Mediterranean $$$

Reserv: Suggested
Dress: Informal
Pay: AE, DC, Disc, M, V
Parking: Yes
Handicap Access: Yes
Bar: Full/separate
Hours: Tu-F 11:30am-2pm,
5-9pm (F 10pm); Sa 4:30-
10pm; Su 4-8pm

348 St Mary's
Pleasanton   925-846-5740

The rebirth of this local favorite has brought on new changes. Expansive windows add air and light to the setting that still has its comfortable booths. The menu has continental leanings but now features many Mediterranean specialties like moussaka, greek salad, pastas, and prawns with feta. Fortunately the early bird specials remain for those who want excellent-value dining, as do the popular prime rib dinners on weekends. Outdoor dining. (13 ratings/mixed)

82 **72** **78** **71**

Nina's Cafe
French $$$

Reserv: Suggested
Dress: Informal
Pay: AE, M, V, Checks
Parking: Yes
Handicap Access: Yes
Bar: Beer/wine
Hours: M-Sa 11:30am-2pm,
5:30-9:30pm

3525 Alameda de las Pulgas
Menlo Park   650-854-6386

Nina's handwritten menu looks like it came from a Parisian bistro: French onion soup, escargots bourgogne, shrimp crepes, salmon en croute, filet of beef, right down to its closing line of "Bon Appetit!" The setting, too, fits the part: Impressionist paintings, lace curtains, intimate cafe tables. And while raters commend the food, they also comment on the personal and friendly service overseen by the two native French owners. (13 ratings/consistent)

81 **77** **82** **75**

O Chame
Japanese $$

Reserv: Accepted
Dress: Informal
Pay: AE, DC, M, V
Parking: Yes
Handicap Access: Yes
Bar: Beer/wine
Hours: M-Sa 11:30am-3pm,
5:30-9pm (F&Sa 9:30pm)

1830 Fourth St
Berkeley   510-841-8783

Complaints about costs are overruled by praises for the elegant improvisations on the Japanese basics where all the details are perfect from the polished wood accents and napkins folded orgami-style to the chopsticks resting on lustrous pebbles and the tactful, accommodating staff. There are two entree choices each day: several "meal in a bowl" soups, and items from the wood oven or grill, all of which are intriguing, high quality, and healthy. Outdoor dining. (37 ratings/consistent)

Food	Service	Ambience	Value

73 **68** **71** **86**

Old Spaghetti Factory $
Italian

Reserv: Not accepted
Dress: Informal
Pay: AE, DC, Disc, M, V, Checks
Parking: No
Handicap Access: Yes
Bar: Full/separate
Hours: M-F 11:30am-2pm,
5-10pm (F 11pm); Sa 4:30-
11pm; Su 4-10pm

51 N San Pedro St
San Jose   408-288-7488

There's no better place to have a family-friendly meal at thrifty prices than this antique-laden restaurant housing an old train car. Usually crowded and boisterous, the menu here is strictly pasta, but has something for everyone. Some complain that the food's only so-so, and activity levels approach those in a beehive, yet no one knocks the pocket-change prices or the extra perks for kids. See Quick-Check Table for highly-rated Oakland location. (25 ratings/very mixed)

81 **76** **80** **71**

Oliveto $$$
Italian

Reserv: Suggested
Dress: Informal
Pay: AE, DC, M, V
Parking: Yes
Area: Rockridge
Handicap Access: Yes
Bar: Full
Hours: M-F 11:30am-2pm,
5:30-10pm; Sa 5:30-10pm;
Su 5-9pm

5655 College Ave
Oakland   510-547-5356

Since the arrival of Chef Paul Bertolli, professionals have heralded the fabulous cuisine served here, and recommend the house-cured meats, pastas, and grilled entrees from the daily-changing menu. Our raters praise the food, but some complain about skimpy portions and high prices. **Honors:** *Focus* Best East Bay and Best Italian, *Wine Spectator*'s Award of Excellence (41 ratings/mixed)

79 **75** **63** **77**

The Original Hick'ry Pit $$$
BBQ

Reserv: Accepted
Dress: Informal
Pay: Disc, M, V
Parking: Yes
Handicap Access: Yes
Bar: Beer/wine
Hours: Daily 6am-10pm (F&Sa
11pm)

980 E Campbell Ave
Campbell   408-371-2400

When you're in the mood for a real "pit stop," head for a booth or counter stool at this lively old-timer where things never change—like the slabs of original pork ribs that are as meaty and tender as they were when your grandparents came here. Breakfast is hefty with eggs, chops, links, and biscuits. And, of course, the PIES. Even the waitresses still call everybody "honey." The prices? Why, still low, of course. (13 ratings/mixed)

| Food | Service | Ambience | Value |

| 78 | 72 | 65 | 84 |

Original Joe's
Italian
$$$

Reserv: Required
Dress: Informal
Pay: DC, M, V
Parking: Valet only
Area: Western Addition
Handicap Access: Yes
Bar: Full
Hours: Daily 10:30am-midnight

144 Taylor St
San Francisco   415-775-4877

This old-timer has built an empire on enormous portions, fabulous grilled burgers and pastas, hearty daily specials, and tuxedo-clad waiters who transport the huge platters of food to hungry patrons. The interior's original too—rows of leatherette booths look out to the open kitchen abuzz with flaming saute pans and chefs on the move. If you're put off by the seedy neighborhood, use the valet parking. (29 ratings/mixed)

| 81 | 78 | 71 | 79 |

Pacific Cafe
Seafood
$$$

Reserv: Not accepted
Dress: Informal
Pay: AE, M, V
Parking: No
Area: Richmond
Handicap Access: Ltd
Bar: Beer/wine
Hours: Daily 5-10pm (F&Sa 11pm)

7000 Geary Blvd
San Francisco   415-387-7091

Consistently excellent fresh fish, moderate prices, and a policy of no reservations means there's usually a line snaking around the block at this low-key cafe. But patrons don't mind—they're treated to free wine while they wait. Once in, order whatever is fresh that day and settle into a comfortable booth for the multi-course simply-prepared meal to follow. Long-standing favorites include the shrimp Louisiana, halibut parmesana, and sand dabs. (33 ratings/consistent)

| 78 | 79 | 83 | 76 |

Palomino
Mediterranean/Bistro
$$$

Reserv: Suggested
Dress: Informal
Pay: AE, DC, Disc, M, V, Checks
Parking: Yes
Area: South of Market
Handicap Access: Yes
Bar: Full/separate
Hours: M-F 11:30am-2:30pm, 5-10pm (F 11pm); Sa&Su 11:30am-4pm, 5-11pm (Su 10pm)

345 Spear St
San Francisco   415-512-7400

You're guaranteed a grand bay view at this waterfront bistro that's as beautiful inside as out. Expansive use of marble, Matisse paintings, and glass sculptures set a stunning scene. The menu revolves around specialties from the wood-burning oven: grilled salmon, roasted chicken, seafood ravioli, thin-crusted pizzas, that people savor as much as the view. An outdoor patio is nice for weekend brunches and for out-of-town guests who want to see it all. (40 ratings/consistent)

| Food | Service | Ambience | Value |

---

80 **70** **64** **77**

Panini
Lunch only
$

Reserv: Not accepted
Dress: Informal
Pay: Checks
Parking: No
Handicap Access: Yes
Bar: None
Hours: M-F 11am-2pm

2115 Allston Way
Berkeley   510-849-0405

Tired of the usual bologna sandwiches? Then this place should hit the spot. How about prosciutto with peas, smoked turkey with white cheddar, or melted mozzarella with coppa? Besides these exquisite sandwiches, round out your meal with daily soups and fruit galettes. The restrictions: you need to be there during weekday lunch hours and be comfortable with self-service. If so, grab a seat in the courtyard and enjoy some of the best sandwiches anywhere. (14 ratings/consistent)

---

84 **80** **79** **70**

Paolo's
Italian
$$$$

Reserv: Suggested
Dress: Coat/tie suggested
Pay: AE, DC, M, V
Parking: Yes
Handicap Access: Yes
Bar: Full/separate
Hours: M-F 11am-2:30pm;
M-Sa 5:30-10pm

333 West San Carlos
San Jose   408-294-2558

This granddaddy of superb food in an elegant atmosphere with river views and located near the Performing Arts Center commands a high price, but many think it's worth it. Upstairs enjoy an apertif in the bar or patio while downstairs dine on the enlivened classics like carpaccio, orrechiette, vitello saltimboca, and cannoli. Try the fixed-price lunch. Live entertainment on weekends. **Honors:** *Wine Spectator*'s Best of Award of Excellence (32 ratings/consistent)

---

85 **80** **82** **76**

Papillon
French
$$$$

Reserv: Suggested
Dress: Coat/tie suggested
Pay: AE, DC, Disc, M, V, Checks
Parking: Yes
Handicap Access: Ltd
Bar: Full
Hours: M-F 11:30am-2pm;
Daily 5:30-9:30pm

37296 Mission Blvd
Fremont   510-793-6331

You'd never suspect that this quasi-adobe building in a sleepy section of Niles proves that continental dining is alive and well, but one order of duck breast, rack of lamb, or crusted salmon and you'll know it's true. Raters give mixed reports, yet say this is a great destination spot for special occasion dining when you want it elegant, have an appetite, and want live guitar music on weekends. (19 ratings/mixed)

80 70 70 83

Pasand Madras Cuisine
Indian $

Reserv: Not accepted
Dress: Informal
Pay: AE, DC, Disc, M, V
Parking: Yes
Handicap Access: Yes
Bar: Beer/wine
Hours: Daily 11:30am-10pm

3701 El Camino Real
Santa Clara   408-241-5150

A good place to awaken your taste buds is this newly expanded restaurant that now hosts live classical music performances on weekends. It also offers excellent dining values in an authentic setting with carved woods and eastern decor. Raters recommend the masala dosas, Andhra specialties, and hail the Pasand special as "one of the best values on the planet." But they warn of one side effect: "we always eat too much here—it's that good." (30 ratings/consistent)

---

74 62 63 79

Pasta Cuisine
Italian $

Reserv: Not accepted
Dress: Informal
Pay: AE, M, V
Parking: Yes
Handicap Access: Yes
Bar: Beer/wine
Hours: Daily 10:30am-8:30pm
(F&Sa 9pm)

2 Theatre Square
Orinda   925-254-5423

The fast food concept is reworked in this pleasant Theatre Square courtyard restaurant where you order at the counter, take a number to your table, and in pronto time, receive a plate of hot pasta. Soups, salads, sandwiches, desserts, and Sunday brunch round out the offerings. Popular items include minestrone, prawns over angel hair pasta, and lasagna. If you want to escape the family atmosphere, try the prepackaged items for takeout. **Honors:** Byrd B/B (14 ratings/mixed)

---

80 73 66 70

Pasta Primavera Cafe
Italian $$

Reserv: Not accepted
Dress: Informal
Pay: AE, DC, Disc, M, V, Checks
Parking: Yes
Handicap Access: Yes
Bar: Beer/wine
Hours: M-Sa 11:30am-9:30pm
(F&Sa 10pm); Su 5-9:30pm

2929 N Main St
Walnut Creek   925-930-7775

This popular cafe was such a hit when it opened that the owners opened another down the street. And another, and another. Now there's an empire of four: all with the same menu and usually packed with the noodle lovers in the area who come for the pasta jambalaya, seafood primavera, and pesto gorgonzola. Several antipasti and salads help pave the way. Both service and atmosphere are casual, and best of all, the prices are extremely reasonable. Outdoor dining. (16 ratings/very consistent)

Food	Service	Ambience	Value

85 **71** **60** **68**

Pauline's Pizza Pie
Pizza $

Reserv: Not accepted
Dress: Informal
Pay: M, V
Parking: No
Area: Mission
Handicap Access: Ltd
Bar: Beer/wine
Hours: Tu-Sa 5-10pm

260 Valencia St
San Francisco   415-552-2050

Like everyone else these days, Pauline's has taken a theme and improvised. That way traditionalists can dine on the classics while the individualists design their own pizzas with all kinds of toppings, and the adventuresome have chevre with salted lemon puree. And Pauline hasn't stopped at making "the best you can get" pizzas, she also offers salads and handmade sorbets and ice creams. Sponged walls, local artwork, and live jazz add an upbeat note. (13 ratings/consistent)

80 **70** **62** **86**

Phnom Penh House
Cambodian $

Reserv: Suggested
Dress: Informal
Pay: M, V
Parking: No
Handicap Access: Yes
Bar: Beer/wine
Hours: M-Sa 11am-9:15pm
(F&Sa 9:45pm)

251 8th St
Oakland 510-893-3825

There's a reason that tables are hard to get at this friendly, small, family-run operation—the food's terrific ("every dish is a treat"), and the dining values are incredible. Start with an order of Cambodian crepe, then work your way into BBQ chicken, pork, beef sticks, or order stuffed eggplant or stir-fry seafood. Just the sheer complexity of ingredients should make you a convert. Then there's the bill—it'll be so low you'll wonder how they do it. (15 ratings/consistent)

86 **71** **61** **91**

Pho 84
Vietnamese $

Reserv: Suggested
Dress: Informal
Pay: M, V
Parking: No
Handicap Access: Yes
Bar: Beer/wine
Hours: M-F 11am-3pm,
5-9pm; Sa noon-9pm; Su 5-9pm

416 13th St
Oakland 510-832-1429

This is bargain dining at its finest from the healthy pho soups, crisp Imperial rolls, and beef salad, to the exotic grilled chicken or chicken sauteed in the chef's aromatic sauce. All attest to the delights of Vietnamese foods that contrast crisp, cool vegetables with hot, savory meats or fish, resulting in some of the most refreshing cuisine in the world. You won't care that the setting and service aren't outstanding; this place is a true steal. (21 ratings/consistent)

Food	Service	Ambience	Value

80 65 69 84   Picante Cocina Mexicana $
Mexican

Reserv: Not accepted
Dress: Informal
Pay: M, V, Checks
Parking: Yes
Handicap Access: Yes
Bar: Beer/wine
Hours: M-F 11am-10pm (F 11pm); Sa&Su 8am-11pm (Su 10pm)

1328 6th St
Berkeley   510-525-3121

Maybe you won't find 17 kinds of margaritas with flags served here, but you will find some of the freshest, homemade specialties around. Even the tortillas are made by hand, and it shows. The food is first-rate and there's a terrific selection of draft beers for the perfect refresher. The interior is spacious and bright with an outdoor patio area, and counter service guarantees a quick meal when you want it. Weekend brunch. (17 ratings/consistent)

81 76 78 78   Pigalle $$$$
French

Reserv: Accepted
Dress: Informal
Pay: M, V, Checks
Parking: Yes
Handicap Access: Yes
Bar: Beer/wine
Hours: M-Sa 11am-9pm (F&Sa 10pm); Su 9am-9pm

27 N Santa Cruz Ave
Los Gatos   408-395-7924

You may have to put up with some noise but raters say that's a small price to pay for the outstanding prix-fixe dinners, lunches, and Sunday brunches of robust country cuisine offered here. Popular dishes include ample portions of boeuf Wellington, canard a l'orange, and sauteed prawns. Illusory painted trompe d'oeil walls covered with street scenes transport you to a charming Left Bank setting. (13 ratings/consistent)

77 78 80 78   Pine Brook Inn $$
German

Reserv: Suggested
Dress: Informal
Pay: AE, M, V
Parking: Yes
Handicap Access: Yes
Bar: Full/separate
Hours: Tu-F 11:30am-2:30pm, 5:30-9pm (F 10pm); Sa 11:30am-10pm; Su 10:30am-2pm brunch, 5-9pm

1015 Alameda de las Pulgas
Belmont   650-591-1735

When your relatives from the old country come to visit, organize a group and meet at this quaint brookside spot with outdoor dining where there's always a party. For birthday celebrations, an organ grinder adds to the festivities, and on Saturdays, you can tap your feet to live music while you dine on knockwurst or wiener schnitzel, and swig a few lagers. After a celebration like this, your guests won't ever want to go home. Brunch is offered on Sunday. (43 ratings/consistent)

Food Service Ambience Value

 **80 69 63 78**

Pizza Rustica Cafe
Pizza $$

Reserv: Suggested
Dress: Informal
Pay: M, V, Checks
Parking: No
Handicap Access: Ltd
Bar: Beer/wine
Hours: Daily 11am-9:30pm

5422 College Ave
Oakland 510-654-1601

If the upstairs menu of international tapas doesn't suit you, go downstairs where you'll find a huge assortment of terrific thin crust pizzas and a broad selection of beers. Pizzas run the gamut from the traditional to the inspirational like Thai chicken, potato-pesto, and Cajun. If you want takeout, a separate menu of rotisserie chicken, salads, and desserts is available individually or in family packs at very reasonable prices. (30 ratings/consistent)

74 66 66 78

Pizzeria Uno
Pizza $$

Reserv: Not accepted
Dress: Informal
Pay: AE, DC, Disc, M, V
Parking: No
Area: Marina
Handicap Access: Yes
Bar: Full
Hours: M-F 11am-11pm (F midnight); Sa&Su noon-10pm

2200 Lombard St
San Francisco 415-563-3144

"Great Chicago-style pizzas!" pair up with soup, salads, pastas, sandwiches, burgers, and wraps, at this diner-style outpost of a national chain whose original owner was the creator of the famed Chicago deep dish pizzas. Today the growing empire has expanded into 28 states, Puerto Rico, and Korea. Popular choices include the "Uno" that's filled with just about everything and the vegetarian Artipaggio. Don't miss the inexpensive express lunch specials. (22 ratings/consistent)

 75 71 65 78

Plearn Thai
Thai $$

Reserv: Suggested
Dress: Informal
Pay: M, V
Parking: No
Handicap Access: Yes
Bar: Beer/wine
Hours: Daily 11:30am-10pm

2050 University Ave
Berkeley 510-841-2148

Plearn's popularity hasn't changed much over the years, so you can expect a wait for a table in a space that's al-ways packed to the gills. However, veteran raters say it's showing its age and could use some revitalization in the kitchen. Despite the complaints, the staff still shines at its vibrant, unusual handling of seafood, like salmon baked in banana leaves, or coconut milk prawns, fragrant house curries and pad Thai mixed noodles. Outdoor dining. (27 ratings/mixed)

Food	Service	Ambience	Value

79 **76** **79** **76**

Pleasanton Hotel $$$
California

Reserv: Suggested
Dress: Informal
Pay: AE, DC, Disc, M, V
Parking: Yes
Handicap Access: Yes
Bar: Full/separate
Hours: M-F 11am-2pm, 5-9pm
(F 10pm); Sa 11am-2:30pm,
5-10pm; Su 10am-2pm,
4:30-9pm

855 Main St
Pleasanton 925-846-8106

Delightful dining in a lovingly restored Victorian marks this historic spot with an innovative menu. Many specialties draw from the Mediterranean like salmon with caponata and couscous, or saffron risotto with seafood, while others have American roots like maple-cured pork chops or Angus steaks. Sunday champagne brunch can be very pleasant on the patio where you're surrounded by greenery. On weekends there's live music. **Honors:** Wrenn B+/B- (32 ratings/consistent)

87 **87** **82** **74**

The Plumed Horse $$$$$
French

Reserv: Suggested
Dress: Coat/tie suggested
Pay: AE, DC, M, V
Parking: Valet
Handicap Access: Yes
Bar: Full/separate
Hours: M-Sa 5-10pm

14555 Big Basin Way
Saratoga 408-867-4711

This converted stable appeals to the well-heeled set who come for refined food, polished service, and rustic atmosphere—with the prices to prove it. Half of the menu changes monthly, but you'll always find rack of lamb, lobster with truffle sauce, and Grand Marnier soufflé. Silks and crackling fires dominate the dining areas, while the rustic bar offers mountain views and live music nightly. **Honors:** *Wine Spectator*'s Grand Award (17 ratings/consistent)

86 **82** **84** **73**

Postrio $$$$
California

Reserv: Required
Dress: Informal
Pay: AE, DC, Disc, M, V
Parking: Valet only
Area: Union Square
Handicap Access: Yes
Bar: Full/separate
Hours: M-F 7-10am, 11:30am-
2pm, 5:30-10pm; Sa 11am-
2pm, 5:30-10pm; Su 9am-2pm,
5:30-10pm

545 Post St
San Francisco 415-776-7825

Stellar foods that echo the city's multi-cultural roots are served in a stunning Kuleto-designed dramatic, bustling setting. Multi-level dining provides something for everyone. The lively bar has its own light menu. An open kitchen produces superb daily dishes like grilled quail with port wine. Sunday brunch is offered and service is solid. **Honors:** *Focus* Best San Francisco Co., *Gourmet, Wine Spectator*'s Best of Award of Excellence (67 ratings/consistent)

Food	Service	Ambience	Value

| 67 | 72 | 66 | 75 |

Pot Sticker
Chinese $$

Reserv: Accepted
Dress: Informal
Pay: AE, DC, M, V
Parking: Yes
Handicap Access: Yes
Bar: Full/separate
Hours: Daily 11am-midnight

3708 S El Camino Real
San Mateo   650-349-0149

This friendly old-timer lives up to its name by serving large, meaty pot stickers with just about everything, from the thriftily-priced multi-course lunch specials to the well presented family dinners with large portions. In addition to their trademark pot stickers, the kitchen produces commendable versions of walnut prawns, lemon chicken, and is particularly adept at handling seafood. Efficient service gets diners in and out in pronto time. (19 ratings/very consistent)

| 82 | 76 | 76 | 76 |

Prima
Italian $$$$

Reserv: Suggested
Dress: Informal
Pay: AE, DC, Disc, M, V
Parking: Yes
Handicap Access: Yes
Bar: Full
Hours: M-Th 11am-3pm,
5-9:30pm; F 11am-10pm;
Sa&Su 5-10pm (Su 9:30pm)

1522 N Main St
Walnut Creek   925-935-7780

Unusual Amalfi specialties pair up with "exceptional wine choices" in this energetic, bustling "trattoria-cum-wine shop" (Cianci) that offers fireside dining, live piano (W-Sa), and an outside patio. Food here can be hit or miss, but plaudits go to the antipasto, pastas, pizza, and grilled veal. A daily tasting menu is also offered. Staff is knowledgeable and receptive.
Honors: Cianci★★, *Wine Spectator*'s Best of Award of Excellence (33 ratings/mixed)

| 77 | 72 | 66 | 76 |

Rasa Sayang
Malaysian $

Reserv: Suggested weekends
Dress: Informal
Pay: AE, M, V
Parking: Yes
Handicap Access: Yes
Bar: Beer/wine
Hours: Tu-Th 11:30am-2:30pm,
5:30-10pm; Sa&Su 11:30am-
3pm, 5-10pm (Su 9:30pm)

977 San Pablo Ave
Albany   510-525-7000

Dreaming of a trip to Malaysia but can't afford it? The pleasant tropical decor is so real you'll feel you're there. The kitchen combines familiar ingredients and spices in unique and exotic ways, yet some raters have complaints. Popular selections include masal vada lentil patties, rasam soup, tandooris, chicken briyani, and masala dosa. Like the setting, the service is casual and breezy. Fixed price lunches. Outdoor dining.
(17 ratings/very mixed)

84	76	75	76

Ristorante Bacco
Italian $$$

Reserv: Required
Dress: Informal
Pay: M, V
Parking: No
Area: Noe Valley
Handicap Access: Yes
Bar: Beer/wine
Hours: M-Sa 5:30-10pm;
Su 5-9:30pm

737 Diamond St
San Francisco 415-282-4969

This neighborhood restaurant packs a punch with its simple vibrant food, friendly Italian waitstaff, and reasonable prices. Some complain of a downhill trend, but high praises go to the pastas like the orecchiette, rigatoni, gnocchi, and risotto that are "a strength of the kitchen," and to grilled entrees like lamb chops that "few places do better" (Bauer) or stuffed chicken. Come early to beat the crowds and the inevitable noise. **Honors:** Bauer★★½ (22 ratings/mixed)

78	76	80	76

Ristorante Ecco
Italian $$$

Reserv: Suggested
Dress: Informal
Pay: AE, DC, M, V, Checks
Parking: No
Area: South of Market
Handicap Access: Yes
Bar: Full/separate
Hours: M-F 11:30am-2:30pm,
6-10pm; Sa 6-10pm

101 South Park
San Francisco 415-495-3291

Everyone loves the setting at this modern, airy oasis overlooking South Park. Sponged walls of warm earth tones bask in light from the soaring windows creating a sleek and comfortable setting. The menu focuses on the more traditional: carpaccio, "marvelous" linguine, stuffed chicken breast, "perfectly done" salmon, and "fork tender" New York steak (Bauer). Save room for dessert, especially the tartufo. **Honors:** Bauer★★½, *Wine Spectator*'s Award of Excellence (21 ratings/consistent)

86	78	75	81

Rivoli
California $$$

Reserv: Suggested
Dress: Informal
Pay: AE, Disc, M, V, Checks
Parking: No
Handicap Access: Yes
Bar: Beer/wine
Hours: M-F 5:30-9:30pm (F
10pm); Sa&Su 5-10pm (Su
9pm)

1539 Solano Ave
Berkeley 510-526-2542

"Really accomplished cooking and it won't leave you broke" report raters who rave about the portobello mushroom fritters, grilled entrees, pastas, risottos, and hot fudge sundaes. The small, cramped quarters are pleasantly decorated and look into a courtyard where you can view wild skunks and raccoons for an added thrill. The wine list is small but well priced. **Honors:** Bauer★★★, Boer A/A-, *Focus* Best East Bay, Himmel★★★★ (61 ratings/consistent)

| Food | Service | Ambience | Value |

| **80** | **75** | **74** | **71** |

Rose Pistola
Italian

$$$

Reserv: Suggested
Dress: Informal
Pay: AE, DC, M, V
Parking: Valet only
Area: North Beach
Handicap Access: Yes
Bar: Full/separate
Hours: Daily 11:30am-midnight (F&Sa 1am)

532 Columbus Ave
San Francisco   415-399-0499

Upbeat and noisy, the Ligurian cuisine served here is a nice change for some, but not for others. Complaints about forgotten reservations, uneven service, and food preparation are offset by compliments about the extensive antipasti, the stellar fish preparations, and interesting desserts. The tasteful interior is very trendy and attracts locals who've made the bar their new hangout. Nightly jazz. Outdoor dining. **Honors:** *Gourmet*, Himmel★★★½ (36 ratings/mixed)

| **80** | **73** | **67** | **77** |

Royal Thai
Thai

$

Reserv: Suggested
Dress: Informal
Pay: AE, DC, M, V
Parking: No
Handicap Access: Ltd
Bar: Beer/wine
Hours: M-F 11am-2:30pm, 5-10pm; Sa&Su 5-10pm

610 3rd St
San Rafael   415-485-1074

Deciding what to have is not easy at this long-standing favorite. The menu is lengthy and much of it shines. Not to be missed are the angel wings that offer "an explosion of flavor," "velvety" chicken coconut soup (Bauer), green papaya salad, pad Thai, and curries that raters warn can be hot. The converted Victorian house provides a nice backdrop for elegant dining, and the silk-clad service is gracious and accommodating. **Honors:** Bauer★★½ (21 ratings/consistent)

| **83** | **81** | **78** | **67** |

Rubicon
French

$$$$$

Reserv: Required
Dress: Informal
Pay: AE, DC, MC, V, Checks
Parking: Valet only (after 6pm)
Area: Financial District
Handicap Access: Yes
Bar: Full
Hours: M-F 11:30am-2:30pm, 5:30-10:30pm (F 11pm); Sa 5:30-11pm

558 Sacramento
San Francisco   415-434-4100

The interior feels like a New York Soho loft with exposed beams, brick walls, and high ceilings. The food too should capture the palates of the designer crowd—truffled scallop salad, sauteed bass with leeks and hazelnuts, and pan-roasted poultry, plus a daily prix-fixe menu. Service that's "still some of the best around" (Bauer) helps offset the high expenses and complaints about noise. **Honors:** Bauer★★★, *Wine Spectator*'s Grand Award (15 ratings/mixed)

Food	Service	Ambience	Value

83 **82** **83** **73**

Rue de Main
French $$$$

Reserv: Suggested
Dress: Coat/tie suggested
Pay: AE, M, V
Parking: Yes
Handicap Access: Yes
Bar: Beer/wine/separate
Hours: M-F 11:30am-2:15pm,
5:30-9:30pm; Sa 5:30-9:30pm

22622 Main St
Hayward   510-537-0812

It's worth a trip to suburbia to experience a meal in this
romantic, intimate setting. Once inside, you're
surrounded by huge murals depicting street scenes of
Paris and an authentic menu of escargots, baked brie,
snapper with capers, salmon with bernaise,
herb-crusted rack of lamb, and tournedos Rossini.
Desserts come highly recommended, as do seasonal
winemaker and special holiday dinners. Classical guitar
serenades on Saturday. (15 ratings/consistent)

86 **81** **78** **78**

Rue de Paris
French $$$$

Reserv: Suggested
Dress: Informal
Pay: AE, DC, Disc, M, V
Parking: Yes
Handicap Access: Yes
Bar: Full/separate
Hours: M-F 11am-2pm, 5:30-
10pm (F 11pm); Sa 5:30-11pm

19 N Market St
San Jose   408-298-0704

There's a long wine list here plus an extensive port
selection that offers vintages back to 1896, so it's not
surprising that the restaurant often has special tasting
dinners. Most, though, come here for the quaint,
romantic atmosphere, and classics like prawns
bordelaise, rack of lamb, salmon filet, and tournedos.
Fixed price dinners are the best value. Outdoor dining.
Honors: *Wine Spectator*'s Award of Excellence
(26 ratings/consistent)

81 **78** **79** **81**

Rumpus
California $$$

Reserv: Suggested
Dress: Informal
Pay: AE, DC, M, V
Parking: No
Area: Union Square
Handicap Access: Yes
Bar: Full/separate
Hours: M-Sa 11:30am-2:30pm,
5:30-10pm (F&Sa 11pm);
Su 5-10pm

One Tillman Place
San Francisco   415-421-2300

"Check pretension at the door," implores this casual
bistro that's fun, lively, and as boisterous as its name.
Though small, the menu offers a range of imaginative
specialties like venison carpaccio, portobello
sandwiches, or chocolate brioche cake at prices that
are reasonable, especially for its convenient high-rent
Union Square location. Staff is friendly and young. Wine
selection is especially good. Outdoor dining.
(18 ratings/consistent)

Food	Service	Ambience	Value

| 80 | 80 | 76 | 71 |

Ruth's Chris Steak House
Steak $$$$$

Reserv: Suggested
Dress: Coat/tie suggested
Pay: AE, DC, M, V
Parking: Valet only
Area: Pacific Heights
Handicap Access: Yes
Bar: Full/separate
Hours: Daily 5-10pm (F&Sa 10:30pm)

1601 Van Ness Ave
San Francisco   415-673-0557

Raters say the steaks here are "the best in the area" and that "no one does them better," but grouse about the high cost of a splurge into the realm of prime beef. The rest of the steakhouse menu is pretty standard and offers no surprises either in listings or quality, though Ruth recommends the stuffed mushroom appetizers and the potatoes au gratin that you can enjoy in the dimly lit clubby setting. **Honors:** *Wine Spectator*'s Award of Excellence (21 ratings/consistent)

| 84 | 77 | 90 | 77 |

Salute Ristorante at Marina Bay
Italian/Seafood $$$

Reserv: Suggested
Dress: Informal
Pay: AE, DC, Disc, M, V, Checks
Parking: Yes
Area: Marina Bay
Handicap Access: Yes
Bar: Full/separate
Hours: M-F 11:30am-10pm; Sa 4-11pm; Su 11am-10pm

1900 Esplanade Dr
Richmond   510-215-0803

The waterfront views and marina setting here cannot be beat. At night San Francisco glitters across the bay, and by day, the local mariners sail by, occasionally stopping in at the bar for a drink, or for a meal. The menu offers a large number of pastas with grilled and sauteed specials. Biggest hits are the penne puttanesca, prawns, braised lamb shanks, and fish specials of the day. The champagne brunch on Sunday is very popular. (14 ratings/very consistent)

| 83 | 79 | 70 | 82 |

Sam's Bar-B-Que
BBQ $$

Reserv: Not accepted
Dress: Informal
Pay: M, V
Parking: Yes
Handicap Access: Yes
Bar: Beer/wine
Hours: M-Sa 11am-9pm

1110 S Bascom
San Jose   408-297-9151

Rib stickin' good BBQ at this great family place that stars at slow cooking over hickory wood. It's a clean sort of joint and there's a little train doing laps near the ceiling. The best approach here is to order up some chicken, ribs, pork, or brisket at the counter, find a table, then roll up your sleeves, and dine like a prince on a pauper's budget. If you're a bluegrass fan, come on Tuesday night and wear your dancing boots. Outdoor dining. (15 ratings/consistent)

Food	Service	Ambience	Value

86 **79** **80** **78**   ### Scala's Bistro   **$$$**
Italian/French

Reserv: Suggested
Dress: Informal
Pay: AE, DC, Disc, M, V
Parking: Yes
Area: Union Square
Handicap Access: Yes
Bar: Full/separate
Hours: M-F 7-10:30am,
11:30am-midnight; Sa&Su 8-
10:30am; 11:30am-midnight

432 Powell St
San Francisco   415-395-8555

It may be noisy, big, and crowded, but it's one of the "in" places to be. Careful attention to detail has given it a real San Francisco feel from the pressed tin ceiling and elaborate plasterwork to the lively upper level bar. Meals are rustic, yet refined, and are based on a fusion of cuisines. Highlights include the ravioli with house-made pesto, seared salmon fillet, an excellent wine list, plus several grappas, eaux de vie, single malts, and cognacs. Open late. (24 ratings/consistent)

81 **76** **74** **70**   ### Scoma's   **$$$$**
Seafood

Reserv: Not accepted
Dress: Informal
Pay: AE, DC, Disc, M, V
Parking: Valet
Area: Fisherman's Wharf
Handicap Access: Yes
Bar: Full/separate
Hours: Daily 11:30am-10:30pm

Pier 47
San Francisco   415-771-4383

Raters hail this seafood house as among the best, admitting that it's overpriced, usually packed, and filled with tourists, but still worth it. Grand portions and ultra-efficient service are draws, as are some of the specialties you don't often encounter elsewhere like abalone, cioppino, or lobster thermidor. The waterfront setting on the piers of Fisherman's Wharf allows diners and out-of-town guests an irresistible view of the bay and Golden Gate beyond. (26 ratings/consistent)

75 **75** **66** **75**   ### Sears Fine Foods   **$**
American

Reserv: Suggested
Dress: Informal
Pay: Cash Only
Parking: No
Area: Union Square
Handicap Access: Yes
Bar: None
Hours: Daily 6:30am-2:30pm

439 Powell St
San Francisco   415-986-1160

The authentic diner's alive and well at this bare bones spot where everything's a vision in pink, from the waitresses' uniforms to the table linens and cafe curtains. The menu, that some term "overrated," is your grandmother's dream: strawberry waffles, french toast, corned beef hash, club sandwiches, and cream of wheat. Offerings include breakfast and lunch only, but the feather light Swedish pancakes served throughout the day keep patrons packing in. (16 ratings/mixed)

Food	Service	Ambience	Value

82 **82** **88** **77**

Shadowbrook
California
$$$

Reserv: Suggested
Dress: Informal
Pay: AE, DC, Disc, M, V, Checks
Parking: Yes
Handicap Access: Yes
Bar: Full/separate
Hours: M-F 5:30-9:30pm;
Sa 4:30-10pm; Su 10am-
2:30pm, 4:30-9pm

1750 Wharf Rd
Capitola   408-475-1511

Ride the quaint funicular to this romantic retreat
hidden on a verdant hillside overlooking Soquel Creek.
Raters say this is a great place to bring your date for a
romantic interlude. Despite some complaints, raters
give high marks to the excellent salmon and fish dishes
and lovely desserts. On weekend evenings, dine to the
strains of a live musical trio, or come for a memorable
Sunday brunch. Outdoor dining. (30 ratings/mixed)

---

88 **85** **90** **75**

Silks—Mandarin Hotel
Asian
$$$$$

Reserv: Required
Dress: Informal
Pay: AE, DC, Disc, M, V, Checks
Parking: Valet only
Area: Financial District
Handicap Access: Yes
Bar: Full/separate
Hours: M-F 6:30-10:30am;
11:30am-2pm, 6-9:30pm;
Sa&Su 7-11am, 6-9:30pm

222 Sansome St
San Francisco   415-986-2020

This exquisitely appointed restaurant offers "luxurious
elements wherever you look" (Bauer) and provides a
beautiful backdrop for its top-ranked fusion cuisine.
Best bets are the "winning" shiitake spring rolls (Unter-
man), crabcakes, seared sea bass, venison, and "four-
star caliber" desserts (Bauer). Luxurious service
follows suit, as do the high prices. **Honors:**
Bauer★★½, *Gourmet*, Unterman★★½, *Wine
Spectator*'s Award of Excellence (15 ratings/consistent)

---

82 **74** **72** **79**

Soizic
Bistro
$$$

Reserv: Suggested
Dress: Informal
Pay: M, V, Checks
Parking: No
Handicap Access: Yes
Bar: Beer/wine
Hours: Tu-F 11:30am-2pm,
5:30-9pm; Sa&Su 5:30-9pm

300 Broadway
Oakland   510-251-8100

The payoff for finding your way to this bistro cafe in a
charmingly remodeled warehouse with its artsy atmosphere is that you get terrific food beautifully presented,
at prices much lower than the big-name restaurants.
Don't miss the warm duck confit salad, "standout"
lamb with Madeira sauce (Davis), penne pasta, and a
roast chicken salad. Friendly service occasionally
missteps. **Honors:** Davis★★½ (19 ratings/consistent)

 Food **Service** **Ambience** **Value**

84	81	77	77

Solano Grill & Bar
East-West $$$

Reserv: Suggested
Dress: Informal
Pay: AE, DC, M, V
Parking: No
Handicap Access: Yes
Bar: Full
Hours: M-Sa 11:30am-3pm,
5-9pm (F&Sa 10pm);
Su 10:30am-3pm, 5-9pm

1133 Solano Ave
Albany   510-525-8686

The latest in fusion food served in a "futuristic-looking dining room" gives this upscale place "an up to the minute feel" (Byrd). Here you'll find salmon or lamb loin with decidedly eastern overtones, or a traditional Mediterranean paella or rack of venison served European style. Be sure to save room for dessert—the chef here goes "all out" (Byrd). Sunday brunch is also offered. **Honors:** Byrd A-/B+, *Wine Spectator*'s Best of Award of Excellence (16 ratings/consistent)

82	77	78	79

South Park Cafe
Bistro $$$

Reserv: Required weekends
Dress: Informal
Pay: AE, M, V
Parking: No
Area: South of Market
Handicap Access: Yes
Bar: Full
Hours: M-F 7:30am-10pm;
Sa 6-10pm

108 South Park
San Francisco   415-495-7275

This popular, cozy, charming bistro offers a bit of Paris with its zinc bar, butter yellow walls, and French newspapers, right next to the park. Lunch is always packed, but things smooth out by the late afternoon when tapas with great french fries and anchovy toasts precede the satisfying dinners of light cod cakes, mussels, wonderful rabbit, duck, and a superb berry tart. Expect lots of noise but service is always attentive and courteous. Outdoor dining. (32 ratings/consistent)

75	79	67	83

Spettro
California $$

Reserv: Accepted
Dress: Informal
Pay: AE, DC, Disc, M, V, Checks
Parking: No
Handicap Access: Yes
Bar: Beer/wine
Hours: Tu-F 11:30am-2pm;
Daily 5-10pm

3355 Lakeshore Ave
Oakland   510-465-8320

Don't be put off by the wacky decor (a real skeleton, mismatched tablecloths, and kid's art on the walls alongside photos of gravestones). The food here is very serious from the stuffed duck legs or coconut lime mussels right down to the child-friendly peanut butter pizzas. Next to the eclectic menu, this place offers friendly service and good values, plus free wine and pizza while you wait for a table. Excellent for family dining. **Honors:** Hamburg★★½ (13 ratings/consistent)

Food	Service	Ambience	Value

81 **73** **74** **73** | ### Spiedini **$$$**
Italian

Reserv: Suggested
Dress: Informal
Pay: AE, DC, M, V
Parking: Yes
Handicap Access: Yes
Bar: Full/separate
Hours: M-F 11:30am-10pm
(F 11pm); Sa 5-11pm;
Su 5-9:30pm

101 Ygnacio Valley Rd
Walnut Creek 925-939-2100

The rotisserie and wood ovens star at this casually elegant trattoria with its upholstered chairs and warm terra cotta walls. Specialties include spit-roasted chicken, duck, and outstanding lamb; pastas such as gnocchi or "light and silky" ravioli (Crum); and "memorable" desserts (Crum). On the downside, some complain that service is about as consistent as a roller coaster ride, and say to beat the inevitable noise "bring earplugs." Outdoor dining. **Honors:** Crum A-/A- (41 ratings/consistent)

83 **80** **84** **76** | ### Splendido **$$$$**
Mediterranean

Reserv: Suggested
Dress: Informal
Pay: AE, DC, Disc, M, V
Parking: Yes
Area: Financial District
Handicap Access: Yes
Bar: Full/separate
Hours: M-F 11:30am-2:30pm,
5:30-10pm; Sa&Su 5:30-10pm

4 Embarcadero Center
San Francisco 415-986-3222

The signature work of Kuleto is evident in this dramatic, exotic place that resembles a medieval Mediterranean fantasyland. The menu draws from the same sun-drenched region and excels at pastas, exceptional oak-roasted mussels and clams, lamb, pan-seared salmon, and the world's best seared pepper tuna. Prices, to some, may be steep, but quantities are ample.
Honors: *Wine Spectator*'s Award of Excellence (36 ratings/mixed)

73 **75** **68** **78** | ### Spoons California Grill **$$**
American

Reserv: Not accepted
Dress: Informal
Pay: AE, DC, Disc, M, V
Parking: Yes
Handicap Access: Yes
Bar: Full/separate
Hours: Daily 11am-11pm
(F&Sa midnight)

1555 S Bascom Ave
Campbell 408-559-7400

Grab a mug filled with a frozen margarita and join the party at this sports bar/taqueria that's full of action and perfect for family fun. The tried-and-true Tex-Mex menu offers plenty of bar foods for all-night snacking, plus a variety of salads and burgers along with all of the south-of-the-border favorites. Something for everyone at everyday prices makes for good deals; happy hour specials can't be beat. Be sure to top it all off with frozen Oreo pie. (15 ratings/consistent)

Food	Service	Ambience	Value

| **84** | **84** | **81** | **84** |

Spring Garden
Chinese
$$

Reserv: Accepted
Dress: Informal
Pay: AE, DC, Disc, M, V
Parking: Yes
Handicap Access: Yes
Bar: Beer/wine
Hours: Daily 11:30am-2:30pm,
4:30-9:30pm

785 Oak Grove Rd
Concord   925-827-1900

Shopping plaza dining can't be better than at this garden setting oasis that scores solidly with raters across the board. A light and airy space filled with live orchids provides an attractive setting for food that's both unusual and first-rate. Seafood specials often contain lobster, and pork usually means tenderloin, while orange chicken receives a splash of Grand Marnier. Daily buffet lunches and weekend brunches offer extra-value dining. Easy parking. (17 ratings/consistent)

| **78** | **75** | **71** | **79** |

Spruzzo!
Italian
$$$

Reserv: Suggested
Dress: Informal
Pay: AE, Disc, M, V, Checks
Parking: Yes
Handicap Access: Yes
Bar: Beer/wine
Hours: M-F 11:30am-2:30pm,
5-10pm; Sa&Su 5-10pm

210 Lafayette Circle
Lafayette   925-284-9709

Wine and pasta pair up with a small menu of antipasti and grilled specialties at this local favorite with a happy following who especially appreciate the good values. House favorites include the gorgonzola cappelletti, linguini with chicken breast, and mixed seafood grill on braised spinach. The casual dining room is small and sometimes crowded, so ask for a table on the patio if the noise gets to be too much. (34 ratings/consistent)

| **80** | **76** | **76** | **78** |

Straits Cafe
Singaporean
$$$

Reserv: Suggested
Dress: Informal
Pay: AE, DC, M, V
Parking: No
Area: Richmond
Handicap Access: Ltd
Bar: Full
Hours: Daily 11:30am-10pm
(F&Sa 11pm)

3300 Geary Blvd
San Francisco   415-668-1783

Exotic eastern cuisine takes you to the crossroads of Asia, and the whimsical tropical decor places you amongst the old storefronts of Singapore at this unusual and friendly place. Specialties range from a fruity yu sang salad with ginger plum dressing or earthy salmon grilled in a banana leaf to pungent sates and tangy chicken curries. Cool it all down with an order of mango mousse, then give the chef a hand—he likes his patrons to be happy. (20 ratings/consistent)

Food	Service	Ambience	Value

82 **75** **76** **74**

Strizzi's
Italian $$$

Reserv: Suggested
Dress: Informal
Pay: AE, M, V
Parking: Yes
Handicap Access: Yes
Bar: Beer/wine
Hours: M-F 11:30am-2pm,
5-9pm (F 10pm); Sa 5-10pm;
Su 5-9pm

1376 E 14th St
San Leandro   510-483-4883

A local favorite that raters praise for its convenient
location, consistently good food, and pleasant service
and ambience. The menu consists of a host of Italian
favorites paired with grilled specialties and first rate
seafood. Look for the grilled salmon or the pastas with
bolognese sauce. Early bird specials featured daily are
value-packed, and there's a special brunch on Sunday.
(23 ratings/very consistent)

81 **73** **68** **79**

Su Hong
Chinese $$

Reserv: Suggested
Dress: Informal
Pay: AE, M, V, Checks
Parking: No
Handicap Access: Yes
Bar: Full/separate
Hours: M-Sa 11:30am-2:30pm,
4:30-9:30pm; Su 4:30-9:30pm

1039 El Camino Real
Menlo Park   650-323-6852

Chicken steals the show at this popular outpost whose
elegant surroundings are a cut above the norm. Look
for the crispy chicken salad, spicy General's chicken,
and Empress chicken, but don't pass up the pot stickers
and pepper beef. Most raters hail the consistently good
food, however, a couple say it's "bland" and "overrated." If you're in a hurry, there's a special take-out
station. Outdoor dining. See Quick-Check Table for
highly-rated Palo Alto location. (36 ratings/mixed)

76 **69** **63** **82**

Sweet Tomatoes
American $

Reserv: Not accepted
Dress: Informal
Pay: DC, Disc, M, V
Parking: Yes
Handicap Access: Yes
Bar: Beer/wine
Hours: Daily 11am-9pm (F&Sa
10pm)

1210 Kifer Rd
Sunnyvale   408-730-8117

This beats fast food for good value all-you-can-eat family dining that's inexpensive and healthy. Patrons
encounter mammoth-sized buffet stations where they
can dine till they drop. There's an extensive salad bar, a
soup and bakery station that raters laud, a large pasta
bar, and, if you still have room, a dessert station that
should tide you over to the next millenium. See Quick-
Check Table for highly-rated Pleasanton location.
(32 ratings/mixed)

80	68	63	72

Tao Tao Cafe $$
Chinese

Reserv: Suggested
Dress: Informal
Pay: AE, DC, M, V
Parking: Yes
Handicap Access: Ltd
Bar: Full/separate
Hours: M-F 11am-2pm,
4-10pm; Sa&Su 4-10pm (Su
9:30pm)

175 S Murphy Ave
Sunnyvale 408-736-3731

If you like Chinese chicken salad, raters say this is the place to go for "the best in the world!" Edging into second place is the Tao Tao beef, though some of the meat specialties and the almond pressed duck receive plaudits as well. The dining room has an elegant feel with plush carpets and soft lighting, while floor-to-ceiling screens create intimate spaces for a relaxed setting. The only downside is that the service can sometimes be disappointing. (32 ratings/mixed)

92	91	95	82

The Terrace at The Ritz-Carlton $$$$
Mediterranean

Reserv: Suggested
Dress: Informal
Pay: AE, DC, Disc, M, V
Parking: Valet only
Area: Nob Hill
Handicap Access: Yes
Bar: Full/separate
Hours: M-Sa 6:30-10:30am,
11:30am-10pm; Su 6:30-10am,
11am-2:30pm, 5:30-10pm

600 Stockton St at California
San Francisco 415-296-7465

"Fabulous! Always!" This is the place where you get it all—the most stellar service the Bay Area has to offer in what raters say is the most beautiful courtyard setting enhanced by gorgeous flowers, a sparkling fountain, and spectacular views of the city. From the kitchen you'll get original creations that rank among the best. And there's live piano music each evening, plus live jazz during the top-notch Sunday brunch. Outdoor dining.
Honors: *Gourmet* (28 ratings/consistent)

80	78	74	82

Three Flames $$$$
American

Reserv: Suggested
Dress: Informal
Pay: AE, M, V
Parking: Yes
Handicap Access: Yes
Bar: Full/separate
Hours: M-F 11am-3pm,
4-10pm; Sa&Su 4-10:30pm

1547 Meridian Ave
San Jose 408-269-3133

"Not gourmet, just great!" raters quip about this largely undiscovered jewel whose quantity, price, taste, and value are hard to beat, especially since you get atmosphere thrown in for good measure. Family-owned and operated, the experienced, long-tenure servers shuttle plates of first-rate salads, seafood saute, and veal specialties to hungry families or those taking a break from the live band and dancing offered nightly except Sunday and Monday. (19 ratings/consistent)

80	66	60	77

Ti-Couz
French (Crepes) $

Reserv: Not accepted
Dress: Informal
Pay: M, V
Parking: No
Area: Mission
Handicap Access: Yes
Bar: Beer/wine
Hours: M-F 11am-11pm;
Sa&Su 10am-11pm (Su 10pm)

3108 16th St
San Francisco 415-252-7373

Brittany comes alive in this charming bistro that's usually packed like a sardine can! Elbow your way through the happy throngs and grab a seat at the counter where you can watch them make the giant buckwheat crepes that are filled with cheeses, meats, ratatouille, vegetables, and seafood. Dessert crepes can be ambrosial. Service is casual and unhurried, so come hungry and when you're not in a rush. **Honors:** *Focus* Best Meal Under $15, Wrenn B/B (35 ratings/very consistent)

84	85	88	70

Tommy Toy's
Chinese $$$$

Reserv: Suggested
Dress: Coat/tie required
Pay: AE, DC, Disc, M, V
Parking: Valet only
Area: Financial District
Handicap Access: Yes
Bar: Full
Hours: M-F 11:30am-2:30pm,
6-9:30pm; Sa&Su 6-9:30pm

655 Montgomery St
San Francisco 415-397-4888

Dining here is like being transported to the extraordinary 19th century sitting room quarters of the Empress Dowager. Royal grandeur too prevails in the food that features foie gras, fillet of beef, lobster, and squab cooked Asian style but presented with French flair. Service receives top marks for its efficiency and poise. For those who find a dinner trip here too costly, a lunch special is served daily. (26 ratings/consistent)

81	73	65	75

Ton Kiang
Chinese $$

Reserv: Suggested
Dress: Informal
Pay: AE, DC, M, V
Parking: No
Area: Richmond
Handicap Access: Yes
Bar: Beer/wine
Hours: Daily 10:30am-10pm

5821 Geary Blvd
San Francisco 415-386-8530

For dim sum "none is better" (Bauer) than you'll find at this run-of-the-mill-looking place. Pot stickers here are "way ahead of the class" (Bauer) and the soft-shelled crab and fried sea bass couldn't be better. Seafood is fresh and sweet. The well-trained staff can help diners who have questions about the new offerings that crop up daily, and, like sushi restaurants, there is now a graphic menu to use as a guide. Weekend brunch. **Honors:** Bauer★★★ (40 ratings/consistent)

81 61 55 75

Tony & Alba's $
Italian

Reserv: Suggested
Dress: Informal
Pay: AE, DC, Disc, M, V, Checks
Parking: Yes
Handicap Access: Yes
Bar: Beer/wine
Hours: Daily 11am-10pm

619 Escuela Ave
Mountain View 650-968-5089

Families, singles, lovers, and seniors share their love for the mile-high pizzas that come out of the ovens of this casual hole-in-the-wall. Besides the ever-popular Tony's special, there's a garlicky Gilroy, chicken Diana, Alba's special with clams, plus pastas, and sandwiches. The decor is bare bones Italian with lots of sports memorabilia on the walls. Value meals are offered for lunch daily and on Sunday to Wednesday evenings.
(13 ratings/mixed)

81 74 77 75

Townhouse Bar & Grill $$$
American

Reserv: Suggested
Dress: Informal
Pay: M, V
Parking: Yes
Handicap Access: Yes
Bar: Full
Hours: M-F 11:30am-2:30pm, 6-9:30pm (F 10pm); Sa 6-10pm

5862 Doyle St
Emeryville 510-652-6151

A lively local spot with outdoor dining, a good bar, nice crowd of people, and live jazz on Thursdays. High marks go to the creative menu, rustic bistro-like atmosphere, and the friendly staff that's occasionally overtaxed. Winning dishes include grilled lamb salad, chicken pot stickers, fried calamari, and roasted pork with calamata olive ragout. Be sure to save room for desserts—raters say they're delicious.
(28 ratings/consistent)

83 79 85 76

Tra Vigne $$$
Italian

Reserv: Suggested
Dress: Informal
Pay: DC, Disc, M, V
Parking: Yes
Handicap Access: Yes
Bar: Full/separate
Hours: Daily 11:30am-10pm

1050 Charter Oak Ave
St Helena 707-963-4444

Raters are divided on this popular wine country destination spot whose interior resembles a stunning Tuscan villa with a vine-covered courtyard and terrace for an outdoor repast. Remarks about food range from "heavenly" to "overrated." Menu highlights include pastas, short ribs, gourmet pizzas, seafood, and daily specials. For out-of-town guests and romantic dining, most think this place is worth the drive and wait.
Honors: *Focus* Best North Bay (67 ratings/mixed)

Food **Service** **Ambience** **Value**

| 85 | 79 | 72 | 76 |

20/30
California/Mediterranean $$$

Reserv: Suggested
Dress: Informal
Pay: AE, DC, Disc, M, V
Parking: Yes
Handicap Access: Yes
Bar: Full/separate
Hours: M-F 11:30am-2:30pm,
5:30-10pm; Sa 5:30-10pm;
Su 5:30-9pm

2030 Broadway
Redwood City   650-363-2030

This "bustling" "urban neighborhood showcase" that's had rough times, is now "happily back on track" (Himmel). The biggest shift is in the menu that's now more Mediterranean, though colossal portions are still a trademark. Highlights include crab cakes, rack of lamb, paella, and daily specials. The setting is pure bistro with exposed brick walls and al fresco dining. Thriftily priced wines. **Honors:** Davis★★, Himmel★★★½
(34 ratings/consistent)

| 87 | 83 | 82 | 73 |

231 Ellsworth
French $$$$

Reserv: Suggested
Dress: Informal
Pay: AE, DC, M, V, Checks
Parking: No
Handicap Access: Yes
Bar: Full
Hours: M-F 11:30am-2pm,
5:30-10pm; Sa 5:30-10pm

231 S Ellsworth St
San Mateo   650-347-7231

The desserts here are dazzling. In fact, everything sparkles with "creativity, whimsy, and skill" and is marked by "style, precision, classical technique, and flavor" (Cianci). Daily prix-fixe and a la carte menus take a light-handed approach to sweetbreads, squab, fish, and game. The sleek interior provides a pleasant stage for stellar service that aims to please. **Honors:** Cianci★★★, *Focus* Best South Bay, *Wine Spectator*'s Best of Award of Excellence (35 ratings/consistent)

| 83 | 84 | 79 | 81 |

Uncle Chung's
Chinese $

Reserv: Accepted
Dress: Informal
Pay: AE, M, V
Parking: Yes
Handicap Access: Yes
Bar: Full
Hours: Daily 11:30am-9:30pm

2550 Appian Way
Pinole   510-222-8881

When the seafood combinations contain abalone and the appetizers are served on flaming hibachis, you know you're getting top-notch Chinese. And indeed, Uncle Chung's is a cut above the norm not only for food, but also for service, lovely bay views, and good dining values. Specialties include fried prawns with walnuts, princess chicken, Mongolian beef, and sweet-and-sour dishes. For the best deals in value dining, try the lunch specials served daily. (15 ratings/consistent)

Food · Service · Ambience · Value

| 76 | 77 | 72 | 76 |

Uncle Yu's
Chinese $$

Reserv: Suggested
Dress: Informal
Pay: AE, DC, Disc, M, V
Parking: Yes
Handicap Access: Yes
Bar: Full/separate
Hours: Daily 11:30am-9:30pm
(F&Sa 10pm)

999 Oak Hill Rd
Lafayette 925-283-1688

A good choice for upscale dining in the 'burbs, this local favorite has a host of regulars who come here for the comfortable atmosphere, personal service, and the food that's prepared in the traditional way but with "neo-classic" overtones. Look for tea-smoked duck, pan-fried lobster tails, rainbow chicken, honey walnut prawns, or BBQ sea bass to witness the kitchen's spin on the usual. A popular spot for family, business, or romantic dining. Outdoor dining. (19 ratings/consistent)

| 80 | 76 | 75 | 79 |

Universal Cafe
California $$$

Reserv: Required
Dress: Informal
Pay: AE, DC, Disc, M, V
Parking: No
Area: Potrero Flat
Handicap Access: Yes
Bar: Beer/wine
Hours: Tu-F 8-10:30am,
11:30am-2:30pm, 6-10pm;
Sa&Su 9am-2:30pm, 6-10pm

2814 19th St
San Francisco 415-821-4608

This cafe used to be known for its award-winning high-tech design. Then along came Julia McClaskey who has lifted it into the realm of restaurant "major leagues" (Unterman). Vibrant combinations include scallop salad, tongue or chicken appetizers, vegetable curry, and pot roast that's "the best in town" (Unterman). The only downsides: the cramped quarters and deafening noise. Weekend brunch. Outdoor dining. **Honors:** *Gourmet*, Himmel★★★½, Unterman★★★ (14 ratings/very consistent)

| 79 | 76 | 76 | 76 |

Vahl's
Italian $$$

Reserv: Accepted
Dress: Informal
Pay: Checks
Parking: Yes
Handicap Access: Yes
Bar: Full
Hours: W-Su 11am-10pm

1513 El Dorado
Alviso 408-262-0731

Having been in operation for nearly six decades, Amelia Vahl knows how to survive. First you get your hands on a lot of sandbags to weather the major floods that come through every few years. Then you concentrate on serving good, plain food like fried chicken, broiled halibut, baked ham, or poached salmon, and lots of it, the same as people liked in the old days. The place looks like it did awhile back, and service is mature and charming. (18 ratings/consistent)

78	**70**	**73**	**75**

Venezia   **$$**
Italian

Reserv: Suggested
Dress: Informal
Pay: AE, DC, M, V, Checks
Parking: Yes
Handicap Access: Yes
Bar: Beer/wine
Hours: M-F 11:30am-2:30pm,
5:30-10pm; Sa&Su 5-10pm (Su
9:30pm)

1799 University Ave
Berkeley   510-849-4681

Half the fun of coming here is that you're "whisked away to a courtyard in Venice" (Hamburg), complete with painted storefronts, a bubbling fountain, and hanging laundry fluttering in the breeze. The other half is the attentive staff and the well-priced tasty Italian food. Try the fritto misto that raters say can't be beat, wonderful pastas, insalata di gorgonzola, gnocchi, and pollo arrosto. A good wine list rounds out the menu. (48 ratings/consistent)

80	**68**	**59**	**76**

Vicolo   **$**
Pizza

Reserv: Not accepted
Dress: Informal
Pay: M, V
Parking: No
Area: Civic Center
Handicap Access: No
Bar: Beer/wine
Hours: M-F 11:30am-2pm,
5-10pm (F 11:30pm); Sa noon-
11:30pm; Su noon-10pm

201 Ivy St
San Francisco   415-863-2382

Head here and join in on the debate as to whether it's the crusts or the toppings that set these pizzas above the rest. Favorites include sausage, wild mushroom, mixed vegetable, and four-cheese, but the menu is so huge, you'll find almost anything imaginable. Great for fast pre-performance meals, but come early—it's usually packed after 6:30. Don't expect ambience: this is semi self-service. (37 ratings/mixed)

68	**72**	**74**	**78**

Villa D' Este   **$$$**
Italian

Reserv: Suggested
Dress: Informal
Pay: AE, Disc, M, V, Checks
Parking: No
Area: Lakeside Village
Handicap Access: No
Bar: Full/separate
Hours: M-F 11:30am-2:30pm,
5-10pm; Sa 5-10pm; Su 11am-
2:30pm, 4-10pm

2623 Ocean Ave
San Francisco   415-334-0580

Raters say the Art Deco setting is worth the trip alone, especially if you go on a weekend when there's live piano music to serenade you through your meal. The food is traditional, to the point of being "tired" to some, but the quantities are ample and the overall values are high, especially since full dinner prices include five courses. Chicken and veal are specialties of the house, and Sunday brunch features eggs, omelets, pastas, and several entrees. (23 ratings/mixed)

Food Service Ambience Value

86	80	81	75

Vivande
Italian $$$

Reserv: Not accepted
Dress: Informal
Pay: AE, DC, Disc, M, V
Parking: No
Area: Pacific Heights
Handicap Access: No
Bar: Beer/wine
Hours: Daily 11:30am-2pm,
5-10pm

2125 Fillmore St
San Francisco   415-346-4430

A friendly trattoria where you can scan the deli case for take-out specialties or grab a seat for dining in. From the small dining area you can watch the nearby kitchen staff prepare some of the best pasta dishes outside of Italy, chicken under bricks, Ligurian seafood stew, daily specials, or maybe one of their outstanding desserts like cannoli and biscotti. Prices are steep but the staff is convivial and there's an excellent wine list to help ease the pain. (21 ratings/consistent)

75	76	64	79

Walker's Pie Shop
American $$

Reserv: Not accepted
Dress: Informal
Pay: Disc, M, V, Checks
Parking: No
Handicap Access: Yes
Bar: Beer/wine
Hours: Tu-Sa 8am-3pm,
5-8pm (F&Sa 9pm); Su 4-8pm

1491 Solano Ave
Albany 510-525-4647

The monthly menu beckons "come home to an Old Friend" and that's how it feels at this local institution. Some come here for the comforting down home classics like fried chicken, smoked ham, or roast lamb. Others come for the modest prices. Many can't resist the real homemade pies mounded with strawberry rhubarb, blueberries, or lemon chiffon. And some simply come for the easy company of others who like to relive the good old days. (34 ratings/consistent)

76	77	68	78

Washington Square Bar & Grill
American $$$

Reserv: Suggested
Dress: Informal
Pay: AE, M, V
Parking: Valet only
Area: North Beach
Handicap Access: Yes
Bar: Full/separate
Hours: Daily 11:30am-11pm

1707 Powell St
San Francisco 415-982-8123

This clubby watering hole is filled with the city's movers and shakers who come here for the extra-dry martinis, the nightly jazz, and the hearty fare that while not the main draw gets the job done. Reliable offerings are usually the simplest, so stick to the calamari, pepper steak, petrale sole, and the foolproof burgers, and keep your eyes on the action—this bustling place is a true San Francisco experience. Sunday brunch. Outdoor dining. **Honors:** Bauer★★ (13 ratings/consistent)

Food | **Service** | **Ambience** | **Value**

| 86 | 83 | 90 | 75 |

Wente Vineyards Restaurant
American $$$$

Reserv: Suggested
Dress: Informal
Pay: AE, Disc, M, V, Checks
Parking: Valet
Handicap Access: Yes
Bar: Full/separate
Hours: M-Sa 11:30am-2:30pm,
5:30-9pm (F&Sa 10pm);
Su 10:30am-2:30pm, 5-9pm

5050 Arroyo Rd
Livermore   925-456-2450

For a beautiful setting, this hacienda-style restaurant "set amid the rolling hills of Livermore Valley's cattle and vineyard country" (Byrd) is unsurpassed. Gaze out over the gardens as you dine on regional American favorites like Caesar salad, house smoked pork chops, or pan-roasted salmon that come a la carte or fixed-price. If prices seem high, try the Sunday brunch for a better value. Outdoor dining. **Honors:** *Wine Spectator*'s Best of Award of Excellence (35 ratings/consistent)

| 87 | 79 | 68 | 79 |

Woodward's Garden
California $$$$

Reserv: Suggested
Dress: Informal
Pay: M, V
Parking: No
Area: Mission
Handicap Access: Yes
Bar: Beer/wine
Hours: W-Su 6-9pm

1700 Mission St
San Francisco   415-621-7122

You're lucky if you can find a seat at one of the 11 tables in this unpretentious bistro where you're so close to the stove you can watch your meal being prepared by the two chefs. The weekly offerings feature five appetizers and five entrees that blend California and Mediterranean influences into one of the most exquisite, original, beautifully presented menus in town. An eclectic wine list complements the meal. (17 ratings/consistent)

| 84 | 73 | 70 | 71 |

Yank Sing
Chinese $$

Reserv: Not accepted
Dress: Informal
Pay: AE, DC, M, V
Parking: No
Area: Financial District
Handicap Access: Yes
Bar: Full/separate
Hours: M-F 11am-3pm; Sa&Su
10am-4pm

427 Battery St
San Francisco   415-362-1640

Dim sum dining on a mega-scale, the teacarts wheel in about 80 different specialties per day. Of those many are standards like tea-smoked duck, snow pea dumplings, or scallion prawns, while others are house specials. Though it's fun to point and choose, the staff is well versed and helpful if you have questions. There's also an area for takeout that's popular with local business clientele who like to eat out of plastic containers at their desks. Weekend brunch. (55 ratings/consistent)

| Food | Service | Ambience | Value |

| 76 | 72 | 68 | 79 |

Yokohama
Japanese

$$$

Reserv: Suggested
Dress: Informal
Pay: M, V
Parking: Yes
Handicap Access: Yes
Bar: Beer/wine
Hours: W-Su 11:30am-2pm,
5:30-9:30pm

11880 San Pablo Ave
El Cerrito   510-234-0821

Tucked in a small shopping center is this local favorite with an indoor garden that offers a peaceful retreat from the suburban bustle outside. Raters say the meals here are "consistently perfect" and recommend the bento boxes and their superior handling of all the classics like sukiyaki, light feathery tempura, and ocean-fresh sashimi. This is the kind of place that needs no fanfare: its reputation is built on consistency and quality. (13 ratings/consistent)

| 86 | 68 | 62 | 81 |

Zachary's Chicago Pizza
Pizza

$

Reserv: Not accepted
Dress: Informal
Pay: Cash Only
Parking: No
Handicap Access: Yes
Bar: Beer/wine
Hours: Daily 11am-10pm
(F&Sa 10:30pm)

5801 College Ave
Oakland   510-655-6385

The hordes waiting at the door tell you this place has fans—a lot of them. They come for the hefty stuffed Chicago pizza that raters find incredible, although the thin-crust pizzas and the Caesar salads shouldn't be overlooked. If you find it too much of a scene and are put off by the waits, especially on weekends, prompt takeout or half-baked pizzas are a good compromise. See Quick-Check Table for highly-rated Berkeley location. **Honors:** Hamburg★★ (27 ratings/mixed)

| 72 | 73 | 64 | 75 |

Zatis
California/Mediterranean

$$

Reserv: Suggested
Dress: Informal
Pay: AE, M, V
Parking: No
Handicap Access: Yes
Bar: Beer/wine
Hours: M-Sa 11:30am-3pm,
5-10pm

4027 Piedmont Ave
Oakland   510-658-8210

The open kitchen along one side of this narrow restaurant allows you to experience everything first hand, yet the atmosphere is intimate and romantic due to soft lighting, jazz, a small number of tables, and white linens. The menu takes an interesting spin on the usual: mussels are sauteed with wine and herbs, lamb kebabs come with lentil-stuffed bell peppers, and eggplant with olives and artichokes is spiked with jalapenos. Service can be uneven. (13 ratings/mixed)

| 78 | 73 | 70 | 76 |

Zza's Trattoria
Italian $$

Reserv: Not accepted
Dress: Informal
Pay: AE, M, V
Parking: No
Handicap Access: Yes
Bar: Beer/wine
Hours: Sa-Tu 4:30-10pm (Sa 11pm); W-F 11am-10pm (F 11pm)

552 Grand Ave
Oakland 510-839-9124

If it's your birthday, they'll turn on the flashing neon sign inside this casual and bustling place, then sing you a song. Otherwise you'll have to enjoy the sidewalk views or create an original work of art from the crayons and butcher paper on your table to add to the others on the wall. Good for families who want it fast and cheap, the menu offers pizzas, salads, pastas, calzone, and several daily specials. Service is young and casual. Outdoor dining. (36 ratings/consistent)

BEST FOOD RATINGS BY CUISINE

(Consumer ratings scores for "food" and "value for your money" shown in parentheses. Listed in "food" score order. Includes only restaurants with "food" score of at least 80 or "value" score of at least 75.)

Afghan

Helmand (87, 85)
Kabul–Sunnyvale (86, 82)
Kabul–San Carlos (81, 81)

American

Wente Vineyards (86, 75)
Eight Forty North First (84, 80)
Max's Diner–San Ramon (83, 81)
Campton Place (83, 69)
Mustards Grill (83, 76)
Boulevard (82, 71)
Eulipia (82, 70)
Carnelian Room (81, 72)
Bold Knight Cattleman's (81, 82)
Flea St Cafe (81, 72)
Townhouse Bar & Grill (81, 75)
Three Flames (80, 82)
Max's Opera Cafe–
    Walnut Creek (80, 80)
Hobee's–San Jose (80, 81)
Birk's (80, 70)
Hobee's–Palo Alto (79, 80)
Fresh Choice–Milpitas (78, 83)
Casa Orinda (78, 75)
Fresh Choice–Sunnyvale (77, 79)

Hobee's–Palo Alto (77, 76)
Max's Opera Cafe–
            San Francisco (77, 75)
Marie Callender's–
            San Jose (76, 80)
Washington Sq. Bar & Grill (76, 78)
Sweet Tomatoes (76, 82)
Max's–Redwood City (76, 78)
Fresh Choice–San Jose (76, 76)
Walker's Pie Shop (75, 79)
Fatapple's–Berkeley (75, 77)
Fatapple's–El Cerrito (75, 75)
Max's Diner–
            San Francisco (75, 75)
Sears Fine Foods (75, 75)
Spoons California Grill (73, 78)
Country Way (73, 84)
Hobee's–Palo Alto (73, 76)
Marie Callender's–
            San Jose (73, 76)
Fresh Choice–Concord (72, 81)
Fresh Choice–Palo Alto (72, 81)
Fresh Choice–San Jose (72, 79)
Fresh Choice–Pleasanton (72, 78)
Abernathy's (72, 77)

Delancy Street (72, 75)
Sweet Tomatoes–
            Pleasanton (71, 81)
Lyon's (71, 77)
Fresh Choice–San Mateo (70, 76)

American (Hofbrau)

Brennan's (68, 83)

Asian

Silks—Mandarin Hotel (88, 75)
Betelnut (85, 78)

BBQ

Sam's Bar-B-Que (83, 82)
Doug's Bar-B-Q (81, 81)
Henry's World Famous
            Hi-Life (80, 80)
The Original Hick'ry Pit (79, 77)
Armadillo Willy's BBQ (78, 76)
Emil Villa's California BBQ–
            Oakland (75, 76)
Emil Villa's California BBQ–
            Hayward (74, 77)
Back Forty Texas BBQ (73, 75)

Basque

Guernica (84, 80)
Basque Cultural Center (78, 82)
Le Chalet Basque (77, 79)
Des Alpes (71, 81)

Bistro

Le Charm (86, 87)
Fringale (85, 78)
Bistro Elan (84, 73)
Le Petit Bistro (83, 81)
South Park Cafe (82, 79)
Soizic (82, 79)
Palomino (78, 76)
City of Paris (77, 79)

Breakfast/Lunch

Jo Ann's Cafe (83, 81)
Cafe Fanny (81, 63)

British

The Garden Grill (84, 69)

Burmese

Nan Yang Rockridge (82, 81)
Mandalay (76, 78)

Cajun

Coleman Still (71, 75)

California

Woodward's Garden (87, 79)
Postrio (86, 73)
Rivoli (86, 81)
20/30 (85, 76)
Auberge du Soleil (85, 73)
The Diner (84, 78)
Manka's Inverness Lodge (84, 64)
Chez Panisse Cafe (84, 71)
Chez Panisse Restaurant (84, 72)
John Ash & Co (83, 76)

Mistral (83, 76)
Lark Creek Inn (83, 73)
The Flying Saucer (83, 79)
Shadowbrook (82, 77)
Moose's (82, 74)
Hawthorne Lane (82, 69)
The Caprice (81, 76)
Garibaldi Cafe (81, 77)
Rumpus (81, 81)
Firefly (81, 74)
Universal Cafe (80, 79)
Garibaldi's (80, 77)
Pleasanton Hotel (79, 76)
Brava Terrace (78, 76)
Christophe (77, 78)
Good Earth–Larkspur (77, 76)
Good Earth–Santa Clara (77, 76)
Spettro (75, 83)
Good Earth–Los Gatos (74, 76)
Zatis (72, 75)

Cambodian

Angkor Wat (82, 81)
The Cambodiana's (81, 81)
Phnom Penh House (80, 86)

Caribbean

Cha Cha Cha (87, 85)

Chinese

Hunan (86, 78)
House of Nanking (85, 84)
Yank Sing (84, 71)
Tommy Toy's (84, 70)
Eliza's–San Francisco (84, 88)
Spring Garden (84, 84)
Uncle Chung's (83, 81)
Eliza's–San Francisco (82, 86)
Mandarin Gourmet (82, 72)

Hong Kong Flower Lounge–
    Millbrae (82, 71)
Hong Kong Flower Lounge–
    San Francisco (81, 75)
Ton Kiang (81, 75)
Su Hong–Menlo Park (81, 79)
China Chili (81, 80)
Tao Tao Cafe (80, 72)
Hong Kong Flower Lounge–
    Millbrae (80, 69)
Chef Chu's (79, 75)
Uncle Yu's (76, 76)
Jade Villa (76, 76)
Gourmet Carousel (75, 86)
Su Hong–Palo Alto (73, 78)
Pot Sticker (67, 75)

Continental

Garden City (88, 75)
Dal Baffo (88, 67)
Iron Gate (88, 75)
Barone's (87, 74)
Bella Vista (83, 69)
Nadine (83, 76)
Bay View Restaurant (82, 77)
Bogie's (82, 71)
Britt-Marie's (81, 79)
The Cape Cod (70, 76)

Deli

Brothers Delicatessen (74, 76)

East-West

Cafe Kati (85, 74)
Solano Grill & Bar (84, 77)

Ethiopian

The Blue Nile (74, 81)

French

Chef Paul's (94, 82)
Le Papillon (93, 81)
French Laundry (93, 77)
Domaine Chandon (91, 75)
Emile's (90, 75)
Fleur de Lys (90, 73)
The Plumed Horse (87, 74)
231 Ellsworth (87, 73)
La Folie (87, 68)
Masa's (87, 69)
Rue de Paris (86, 78)
Scala's Bistro (86, 78)
Le Maconnais (86, 89)
Luzern (86, 86)
Le Mouton Noir (86, 73)
Chez TJ (86, 69)
Le Marquis (85, 77)
Papillon (85, 76)
La Cocotte (84, 76)
La Bergerie (83, 84)
Rue de Main (83, 73)
Rubicon (83, 67)
Nina's Cafe (82, 71)
El Paseo (82, 74)
Christophe (82, 79)
Anjou (81, 78)
Pigalle (81, 78)
French Room (81, 77)
La Creme de la Creme (80, 78)
Le Cyrano (80, 81)
Le Central (80, 73)
Bistro Clovis (80, 76)

French (Crepes)

Ti-Couz (80, 77)

German

Pine Brook Inn (77, 78)

Greek

Evvia (82, 73)

Indian

Ajanta (84, 80)
Gaylord India (81, 71)
Pasand Madras Cuisine (80, 83)
Maharani (73, 75)

Italian

Scala's Bistro (86, 78)
Vivande (86, 75)
Buon Gusto (86, 73)
Montecatini (85, 82)
Salute Ristorante
    at Marina Bay (84, 77)
La Pastaia—De Anza Hotel (84, 74)
Ristorante Bacco (84, 76)
Paolo's (84, 70)
Laghi (83, 74)
Massimo's (83, 79)
Tra Vigne (83, 76)
Prima (82, 76)
Cafc Riggio (82, 78)
Strizzi's (82, 74)
Oliveto (81, 71)
Spiedini (81, 73)
Tony & Alba's (81, 75)
Il Fornaio (81, 76)
Pasta Primavera Cafe (80, 70)
Italian Colors (80, 82)
Aperto (80, 80)
Rose Pistola (80, 71)
Gira Polli (79, 80)
Vahl's (79, 76)
Ristorante Ecco (78, 76)
Casa Orinda (78, 75)
Venezia (78, 75)
Spruzzo! (78, 79)

Original Joe's (78, 84)
Zza's Trattoria (78, 76)
Fabrizio's (77, 78)
Cafe Enrico (77, 80)
Caffe Delle Stelle (75, 75)
Pasta Cuisine (74, 79)
Di Cicco's (73, 76)
Joe's of Westlake (73, 77)
Old Spaghetti Factory–
    San Jose (73, 86)
Banchero's (72, 85)
Capp's Corner (71, 77)
Villa D' Este (68, 78)
Old Spaghetti Factory–
    Oakland (65, 75)

Japanese

Kirala (87, 74)
Miraku (85, 78)
O Chame (81, 75)
Fuki Sushi (80, 69)
Yokohama (76, 79)
Mifune (74, 77)

Latin American

Cafe de la Paz (74, 76)

Malaysian

Rasa Sayang (77, 76)

Mediterranean

The Terrace at
    The Ritz-Carlton (92, 82)
20/30 (85, 76)
Citron (84, 75)
Lalime's (84, 79)
Mistral (83, 76)
Splendido (83, 76)

Bay Wolf (82, 75)
Moose's (82, 74)
Aperto (80, 80)
Garibaldi's (80, 77)
Little City Antipasti Bar (78, 76)
Palomino (78, 76)
New Rochelle (73, 79)
Zatis (72, 75)

Mexican

La Taqueria (85, 89)
The Diner (84, 78)
La Fiesta (83, 82)
Andale–Palo Alto (81, 83)
Picante Cocina Mexicana (80, 84)
Andale–Los Gatos (80, 86)
Chevy's (76, 75)
La Pinata (75, 78)
Celia's (75, 76)
Cactus Taqueria (74, 75)
Mom Is Cooking (74, 77)
Line-Up (73, 76)
El Torito (72, 75)
CC Ole's (69, 78)

Middle Eastern

La Mediterranee (77, 87)

Pizza

Zachary's Chicago Pizza–
    Oakland (86, 81)
Applewood Inn (85, 79)
Pauline's Pizza Pie (85, 68)
Zachary's Chicago Pizza–
    Berkeley (81, 79)
Pizza Rustica Cafe (80, 78)
Vicolo (80, 76)
Pizzeria Uno (74, 78)

Seafood

Salute Ristorante
  at Marina Bay (84, 77)
Scoma's (81, 70)
Pacific Cafe (81, 79)
Aqua (80, 59)
Kincaid's Bay House (79, 75)
Lou's Village (78, 75)

Singaporean

Straits Cafe (80, 78)

Spanish

Iberia (83, 73)
Esperpento (76, 77)

Steak

Izzy's (84, 76)
Alfred's (83, 78)
House of Prime Rib (82, 78)
Harris' (80, 69)
Hungry Hunter–S San Fran (80, 73)
Ruth's Chris Steak House (80, 71)

Hungry Hunter–Concord (79, 76)
Hungry Hunter–Pleasanton (78, 76)

Swiss

Luzern (86, 86)

Thai

Khan Toke Thai House (83, 82)
Lemon Grass (83, 83)
Royal Thai (80, 77)
Cha-Am (80, 75)
Boran Thai (78, 78)
Plearn Thai (75, 78)

Vegetarian

Long Life Vegi House (69, 77)

Vietnamese

Pho 84 (86, 91)
Golden Turtle (81, 77)
Mama Lan's (80, 74)
Le Cheval (77, 80)

RESTAURANTS WITH SELECTED SPECIAL FEATURES

(Selected from among the top-rated restaurants whose write-ups appear on pages 29–115.)

Weekend Brunch

Andale (Sa, Su)
Aperto (Sa, Su)
Cafe de la Paz (Sa, Su)
Campton Place (Su)
The Caprice (Su)
Carnelian Room (Su)
CC Ole's (Sa, Su)
City of Paris (Sa, Su)
Delancy Street (Sa, Su)
El Torito (Su)
Flea St Cafe (Su)
French Room (Su)
Fresh Choice (Su)
Garibaldi's (Su)
Gaylord India (Su)
Good Earth (Sa, Su)
Il Fornaio (Sa, Su)
John Ash & Co (Su)
Kincaid's Bay House (Su)
La Creme de la Creme (Su)
La Fiesta (Sa, Su)
La Mediterranee (Sa, Su)
Lark Creek Inn (Su)
Le Mouton Noir (Sa)
Line-Up (Su)
Little City Antipasti Bar (Su)
Lyon's (Sa, Su)
Marie Callender's (Su)
Moose's (Su)

Palomino (Sa, Su)
Pasta Cuisine (Su)
Picante Cocina Mexicana (Sa, Su)
Pigalle (Su)
Pine Brook Inn (Su)
Pleasanton Hotel (Su)
Postrio (Su)
Salute Ristorante at Marina Bay (Su)
Shadowbrook (Su)
Solano Grill & Bar (Su)
Spring Garden (Sa, Su)
Strizzi's (Su)
The Terrace at The Ritz-Carlton (Su)
Ton Kiang (Sa, Su)
Universal Cafe (Sa, Su)
Villa D' Este (Su)
Washington Square Bar & Grill (Su)
Wente Vineyards Restaurant (Su)
Yank Sing (Sa, Su)

Open Late

(After 11pm at least one night a week)

Betelnut
Cha Cha Cha
Chef Paul's
Chez Panisse Cafe
Di Cicco's
Doug's Bar-B-Q
El Torito

Il Fornaio
Joe's of Westlake
Little City Antipasti Bar
Lyon's
Moose's
Original Joe's
Pizzeria Uno
Pot Sticker
Rose Pistola
Scala's Bistro
Spoons California Grill

Entertainment

*(Every night unless
otherwise noted)*

Abernathy's
Angkor Wat (F&Sa)
Barone's (F&Sa)
Bay View Restaurant (Sa)
Bogie's (Tu)
Bold Knight Cattleman's (W-Sa)
Brennan's (F&Sa)
Celia's (W)
Chez TJ
China Chili
Di Cicco's (W&Sa)
French Room (W-Su)
Garden City
Harris' (W-Sa)
Hawthorne Lane
Iron Gate (F&Sa)
Italian Colors (Th-Sa)
Joe's of Westlake
Khan Toke Thai House (Su)
Little City Antipasti Bar (M,F,Su)
Manka's Inverness Lodge (call)
Max's Opera Cafe
Moose's
Paolo's (F&Sa)
Papillon (F&Sa)

Pasand Madras Cuisine (F&Sa)
Pauline's Pizza Pie (1st Th of month)
Pine Brook Inn (F&Sa)
Pleasanton Hotel (F-Su)
The Plumed Horse
Prima (W-Sa)
Rose Pistola
Rue de Main (Sa)
Sam's Bar-B-Que (Tu)
Shadowbrook (F&Sa)
The Terrace at The Ritz-Carlton
Three Flames (Tu-Sa)
Townhouse Bar & Grill (Th)
Vahl's (Sa)
Villa D' Este (F-Su)
Washington Square Bar & Grill

Outdoor Dining

Abernathy's
Alfred's
Andale
Anjou
Auberge du Soleil
Barone's
Bay Wolf
Betelnut
Bistro Elan
Brava Terrace
Brothers Delicatessen
Cactus Taqueria
Cafe Fanny
The Cape Cod
The Caprice
Chef Chu's
Chef Paul's
Chevy's
Chez TJ
Citron
Delancy Street
Domaine Chandon

El Paseo
Esperpento
Eulipia
Fabrizio's
Flea St Cafe
The Flying Saucer
French Laundry
French Room
Fresh Choice
Fuki Sushi
The Garden Grill
Garibaldi Cafe
Good Earth
Iberia
Italian Colors
John Ash & Co
La Cocotte
La Creme de la Creme
La Fiesta
La Mediterranee
La Pastaia—De Anza Hotel
La Taqueria
Lark Creek Inn
Le Chalet Basque
Le Charm
Le Maconnais
Le Marquis
Le Mouton Noir
Little City Antipasti Bar
Massimo's
Max's
Max's Diner
Max's Opera Cafe
Miraku
Mistral
Mom Is Cooking
Nan Yang Rockridge
New Rochelle
O Chame
Palomino
Panini

Paolo's
Pasta Cuisine
Pasta Primavera Cafe
Picante Cocina Mexicana
Pine Brook Inn
Plearn Thai
Pleasanton Hotel
Prima
Rasa Sayang
Rose Pistola
Rue de Paris
Rumpus
Sam's Bar-B-Que
Shadowbrook
South Park Cafe
Spiedini
Spruzzo!
Su Hong
The Terrace at The Ritz-Carlton
Townhouse Bar & Grill
Tra Vigne
20/30
Uncle Yu's
Universal Cafe
Washington Square Bar & Grill
Wente Vineyards Restaurant
Zza's Trattoria

Scenic View

Auberge du Soleil
Bay View Restaurant
Bella Vista
Boulevard
Brava Terrace
Cafe Enrico
The Caprice
Carnelian Room
Delancy Street
John Ash & Co
Kincaid's Bay House

Little City Antipasti Bar
Mistral
Palomino
Paolo's
Pine Brook Inn
The Plumed Horse
Ristorante Ecco
Salute Ristorante at Marina Bay
Scoma's
Shadowbrook
Spiedini
The Terrace at The Ritz-Carlton
Tra Vigne
Uncle Chung's
Wente Vineyards Restaurant
Zza's Trattoria

Pizza Rustica Cafe
Pizzeria Uno (Service)
Pleasanton Hotel (Service)
Rue de Paris (Service)
Solano Grill & Bar (Service)
Spoons California Grill (Service)
Spruzzo!
Straits Cafe (Service)
Ton Kiang
Tony & Alba's
Uncle Yu's (Service)
Vicolo (Service)
Vivande
Yank Sing (Service)

Home Delivery Available

Abernathy's (Service)
Angkor Wat (Service)
Applewood Inn (Service)
Cactus Taqueria (Service)
CC Ole's (Service)
Chevy's
Emil Villa's California BBQ (Service)
Fresh Choice
Garibaldi Cafe (Service)
Gaylord India (Service)
Gira Polli
Golden Turtle (Service)
Good Earth (Service)
Izzy's (Service)
Jade Villa
Maharani (Service)
Mandalay
Mandarin Gourmet (Service)
Max's (Service)
Mistral (Service)
Mustards Grill (Service)
Original Joe's (Service)
Pine Brook Inn (Service)

Takeout Available

Abernathy's
Ajanta
Alfred's
Andale
Angkor Wat
Aperto
Applewood Inn
Armadillo Willy's BBQ
Back Forty Texas BBQ
Banchero's
Barone's
Bella Vista
Betelnut
Bistro Elan
Bold Knight Cattleman's
Boran.Thai
Brava Terrace
Brennan's
Britt-Marie's
Brothers Delicatessen
Buon Gusto
Cactus Taqueria
Cafe de la Paz
Cafe Enrico
Cafe Fanny

Cafe Riggio
Caffe Delle Stelle
The Cambodiana's
Capp's Corner
The Caprice
Casa Orinda
CC Ole's
Celia's
Cha Cha Cha
Chef Chu's
Chef Paul's
Chevy's
China Chili
Citron
City of Paris
Coleman Still
The Diner
Doug's Bar-B-Q
Eight Forty North First
El Torito
Eliza's
Emil Villa's California BBQ
Esperpento
Eulipia
Fabrizio's
Fatapple's
Firefly
Flea St Cafe
Fresh Choice
Fuki Sushi
The Garden Grill
Garibaldi Cafe
Garibaldi's
Gaylord India
Gira Polli
Golden Turtle
Good Earth
Gourmet Carousel
Guernica
Henry's World Famous Hi-Life
Hobee's

Hong Kong Flower Lounge
House of Nanking
House of Prime Rib
Hunan
Hungry Hunter
Iberia
Il Fornaio
Iron Gate
Italian Colors
Izzy's
Jade Villa
Jo Ann's Cafe
Joe's of Westlake
Kabul
Khan Toke Thai House
Kincaid's Bay House
La Creme de la Creme
La Fiesta
La Mediterranee
La Pastaia—De Anza Hotel
La Pinata
La Taqueria
Laghi
Le Central
Le Cheval
Le Maconnais
Le Marquis
Le Mouton Noir
Le Petit Bistro
Lemon Grass
Line-Up
Little City Antipasti Bar
Long Life Vegi House
Lou's Village
Lyon's
Maharani
Mama Lan's
Mandalay
Mandarin Gourmet
Marie Callender's
Massimo's

Max's
Max's Diner
Mifune
Miraku
Mistral
Mom Is Cooking
Mustards Grill
Nan Yang Rockridge
Nina's Cafe
O Chame
Old Spaghetti Factory
The Original Hick'ry Pit
Original Joe's
Panini
Paolo's
Pasand Madras Cuisine
Pasta Cuisine
Pasta Primavera Cafe
Pauline's Pizza Pie
Phnom Penh House
Pho 84
Pigalle
Pine Brook Inn
Pizza Rustica Cafe
Pizzeria Uno
Plearn Thai
Pleasanton Hotel
Pot Sticker
Rasa Sayang
Ristorante Bacco
Ristorante Ecco
Rose Pistola
Royal Thai
Rue de Main
Rumpus
Salute Ristorante at Marina Bay

Sam's Bar-B-Que
Scala's Bistro
Scoma's
Sears Fine Foods
Soizic
South Park Cafe
Spettro
Spiedini
Spoons California Grill
Spring Garden
Straits Cafe
Strizzi's
Su Hong
Sweet Tomatoes
Tao Tao Cafe
The Terrace at The Ritz-Carlton
Three Flames
Ton Kiang
Tony & Alba's
Townhouse Bar & Grill
20/30
Uncle Chung's
Uncle Yu's
Universal Cafe
Vahl's
Venezia
Vicolo
Villa D' Este
Vivande
Walker's Pie Shop
Washington Square Bar & Grill
Wente Vineyards Restaurant
Yank Sing
Zachary's Chicago Pizza
Zatis
Zza's Trattoria